WO

'A dramatic symbolised version of female revolt'
– *Guardian*

'Saadawi writes with vigour and rage' – *Spare Rib*

This bestseller . . . turns a savage eye not only on kings,
princes and rulers, husbands, fathers and lovers, but on
their God' – *City Limits*

'Scorching' – *New Internationalist*

'Woman at Point Zero should begin the long march
towards a realistic and sympathetic portrayal of
Arab women' – *Middle East International*

GOD DIES BY THE NILE

'Nawal El Saadawi writes with directness and passion,
transforming the systematic brutalisation of peasants and
of women into powerful allegory'
– *New York Times Book Review*

'A quietly formidable achievement; its understated
evocation of tragedy and strength in the face of
victimisation make it a graceful classic' – *Women's Review*

'Powerfully political' – *Poetry Nation Review*

'Nawal El Saadawi's achievement is to lay bare the thin
flesh and huge passions of her characters'
– *West Indian Digest*

NAWAL EL SAADAWI

Nawal El Saadawi – Egyptian novelist, doctor and militant writer on Arab women's problems and their struggle for liberation – was born in the village of Kafr Tahla. Refusing to accept the limitations imposed by both religious and colonial oppression on most women of rural origin, she qualified as a doctor in 1955 and rose to become Egypt's Director of Public Health. Since she began to write over 25 years ago, her books have concentrated on women. In 1972, her first work of non-fiction, *Women and Sex*, evoked the antagonism of highly placed political and theological authorities, and the Ministry of Health was pressurised into dismissing her. Under similar pressures she lost her post as Chief Editor of a health journal and as Assistant General Secretary in the Medical Association in Egypt. From 1973 to 1976 she worked on researching women and neurosis in the Ain Shams University's Faculty of Medicine; and from 1979 to 1980 she was the United Nations Advisor for the Women's Programme in Africa (ECA) and Middle East (ECWA). Later in 1980, as a culmination of the long war she had fought for Egyptian women's social and intellectual freedom – an activity that had closed all avenues of official jobs to her – she was imprisoned under the Sadat regime. She has since devoted her time to being a writer, journalist and worldwide speaker on women's issues.

With the publication by Zed Books in 1980 of *The Hidden Face of Eve: Women in the Arab World*, English-language readers were first introduced to the work of Nawal El Saadawi. Zed Books has also published two of her previous novels, *Woman at Point Zero* (1983) and *God Dies by the Nile* (1985). Nawal El Saadawi has received three literary awards.

Nawal El Saadawi
The Circling Song

Translated from the Arabic

Zed Books Ltd
London and New Jersey

The Circling Song was originally published in Arabic.
It was first published in English by Zed Books Ltd.,
57 Caledonian Road, London N1 9BU, United Kingdom,
and 171 First Avenue, Atlantic Highlands,
New Jersey 07716, USA, in 1989

Copyright © Nawal El Saadawi, 1989
Translation copyright © Zed Books Ltd. 1989

Typeset by AKM Associates (UK) Ltd.
Cover design by Andrew Corbett
Cover illustration by Phyllis Mahon
Printed and bound in the United Kingdom by
Cox and Wyman Ltd., Reading

British Library Cataloguing in Publication Data

Saadawi, Nawal
  The circling song.
  I. Title   II. Ughniyat al-atfal al-da'iriyah.
  English
  892'.736 [F]

  ISBN 0-86232-816-0
  ISBN 0-86232-817-9 pbk

Library of Congress Cataloging in Publication Data

Sa'dāwī, Nawāl.
  The circling song.

  Translation of: Ughniyat al-atfāl al-dā'iriyah.
  I. Title
PJ7862.A3U3813   1989   892'.736   88-29782

ISBN 0-86232-816-0
ISBN 0-86232-817-9 (pbk.)

Dedication

Centuries ago, and all alone, I gave birth to an unknown child. That night I relinquished him to the canal embankment's sheltering embrace, and the next morning I found in his place a towering green tree. Sending its roots into the earth and lifting its crown into the sky, that tree was as lofty as the ancient goddess of life and death.

To that child, to all of the world's towering trees, and to all of the children born of gods, I dedicate this story.

Nawal El Saadawi

Author's Introduction

Among the novels I have written, *The Circling Song* is one of the closest to my heart. I wrote it at the end of 1973 – in November, I'm quite sure – when I was going through a period marked by an enigmatic, internal sadness. Egypt's ruler at that time was extremely pleased with, and proud of, his victories; he was surrounded by a large entourage of men, and some women, all of whom applauded him for whatever reason, and perhaps without any reason.

It was not clear to me what the principal source of my melancholy was, but there certainly were some external reasons that contributed: being deprived of my position and summarily dismissed from my job the year before (in August 1972) because of some of my published writings; the confiscation of my books and articles; and the inclusion of my name on the government's blacklist. Meanwhile, every morning I saw the face of Egypt's ruler printed on newspaper and magazine pages, and I could hear his voice reverberating from various microphones.

No affiliation or contact linked me with politics or the ruling establishment, or with the ruler. I was writing all the

1

time, and carrying on my medical practice on a part-time basis. But a relationship of sorts developed between the ruler and me (from one side, of course); it was an association based on hatred. I had not experienced hatred before in that way: at the time, most of my relationships were ones built on affection.

From time to time, I visited my village, Kafr Tahla. There I would feel a sense of relief and relaxation as I sat in my father's very modest old house, which was almost bare of furnishings. I would smell the fragrance of its dirt floor, newly sprinkled by my cousin Zaynab to keep the dust down. I would see the faces of the children, both girls and boys, looking like flowers just as they open, covered with flies as bees cover a blossom. I would hear them singing as they played atop the dung heaps.

One of their songs was 'Hamida had a baby . . .' I used to hear them frequently as they sang it, and I had heard it many times before as a child, as one of them. I don't know why, when I heard them singing it this particular time, the song inspired me with the idea behind this novel.

The idea was vague and cryptic, and profound; it kept me from sleeping for several days, or perhaps weeks. Then I began to write. Carrying my papers inside a cloth tote bag and wearing my leather sandals – since they had flexible, rubber-like soles – I would leave my house on Murad Street in Giza, just across the river from Cairo. It would take me about half an hour to traverse Nile Street, cross the Cairo University Bridge, and reach my destination: a small, outdoor garden café by the Nile, since demolished to make way for the Fire Department. Seated on a bamboo chair, a little bamboo table before me, I would gaze at the waters of the Nile and write.

I wrote the first draft of the novel in a few weeks, and rewrote it in a few days. As I wrote certain sections, I could feel the tears on my face. When Hamida (or Hamido) felt tears, I felt my own. I was sure that my novel would amount to something, for as long as I was crying real tears along with the characters of the novel, then surely this work was artistically alive, and would have a similar effect on those who read it.

Whenever I heard the microphones and broadcasts bellowing out their joyous songs, my sadness would grow. I didn't know which of the two emotions held more reality: the joy of the world around me, or the sadness inside. I felt that this world and I were utterly incompatible, and the novel was simply an attempt to give that incompatibility concrete form.

I couldn't publish this novel in Egypt, of course, since I was on the government's blacklist. So I tried to publish it in Beirut. At that time, Beirut was like a lung which gave many writers – men and women prohibited from publishing – ability to breathe.

Dar al-Adab published the novel in Beirut two or three years – I don't remember exactly – after I had written it. In Egypt, naturally, the critics ignored it. Perhaps they even avoided reading it, for this was the treatment they had consistently given my other books. Thus, the novel came out in an atmosphere of silence, and it has lived in the same silence to the present. But people did read it, because the publisher in Beirut reprinted it more than once, and because one of the publishers in Egypt also has published it several times (since 1982). But the critics in Egypt maintained their silence, while the novel continued to be published and read in Egypt as well as in other Arab countries.

Meanwhile, I had forgotten this novel completely and had written other novels in a very different style. Yet the characteristics and structure of this particular novel lived on in my imagination, like a dream that one has once had. I wanted to write another, perhaps a more ambitious novel that would draw upon the same way of writing. And from time to time I would meet a woman or man who had read it, or receive a letter from a reader – sometimes a woman, sometimes a man – making a comment about this novel along the lines of 'This

3

little book has released so many of my innermost feelings! Why don't you always write in this style?'

But every idea has its own particular mode of expression, and I made no attempt to impose this style on different thoughts or ideas.

One day when I was in London, the publisher of this novel asked me if I had a new novel which could be translated and published. I don't know why this particular work came to mind immediately – this novel which had been published in Arabic for the first time more than a decade before in Beirut. I realized that I was very fond of *The Circling Song*, and that it was like the sort of close relationship which one does not forget no matter how many years pass. I hadn't read the novel for ten years, as I don't like to read my books after they are published, but the translator of this novel gave me a copy of the translation for me to review. The strangest thing happened: it seemed as if I were reading it for the first time. I would stop at certain sections, surprised, as if the writer were another woman, someone other than me. Indeed – and how peculiar this seemed – I felt actual tears coming whenever Hamida (or Hamido) cried. And this is how I knew that the translation was as I wished it to be.

Nawal El Saadawi
Cairo, 1989

The Circling Song

Every day, and at whatever time I left the house, my gaze was met by a ring of little bodies, winding round and round, circling continuously before my eyes. The children's thin, high-pitched voices spiralled palpably up into the sky. The rhythmic orbit of their singing was synchronized with the movement of their bodies, fused into a single song, comprised of one stanza which repeated itself in a never-ending, unbroken cycle, as they turned round and round, and round:

Hamida had a baby,
She named him Abd el-Samad,*
She left him by the canal bed,
The kite swooped down and snatched off his head!
Shoo! Shoo! Away with you!
O kite, O monkey snout!
Hamida had a baby,
She named him Abd el-Samad,
She left him by the canal bed,
The kite swooped down and snatched off his head!
Shoo! Shoo! Away with you!

O kite, O monkey snout!
Hamida had a baby,
She named him Abd el-Samad . . .

The children would repeat the song, so rapidly that the first line sounded before the echo of the last had died down, and the last line seemed to follow fast on the tail of the first. Because they were circling and singing uninterruptedly, it was impossible to pick out the song's beginning or end by ear. And since they were grasping each other tightly by the hand as children are wont to do, one could not tell by looking where the circle began and where it ended.

But everything does have a beginning, and so if I am to tell this story I must begin. Yet I do not know the starting point of my tale. I am unable to define it precisely, for the beginning is not a point that stands out clearly. In fact, there is no beginning, or perhaps it would be more accurate to say that the beginning and the end are adjoined in a single, looping strand; where that thread starts and where it ends can be discerned only with great difficulty.

Here lies the difficulty of all beginnings, especially the beginning of a true story, of a story as truthful as truth itself, and as exact in its finest details as exactitude itself. Such exactitude requires of the author that he or she neither omit nor neglect a single point. For, in the Arabic language, even one point – a single dot – can completely change the essence of a word. Male becomes female because of a single dash or dot. Similarly, in Arabic the difference between 'husband' and 'mule', or between 'promise' and 'scoundrel', is no more than a single dot placed over a single form, an addition which transforms one letter into another.

So I must begin my story at a well-defined point. And a well-defined point is just that and nothing else. It cannot be a dash or a circle, for instance, but rather must be a real point in the full geometrical sense of the word. In other words, scientific accuracy is unavoidable in this work of art which is my novel. But scientific acccuracy can corrupt or distort a work of art. Yet perhaps that corruption or distortion is exactly what I want, and what I aim for in this story. Only then will it be as truthful, sincere and real as 'living life'. This is an expression upon which I insist; I write it deliberately, with premeditation: it is not a haphazard or accidental choice. For there are two kinds of life: 'living life' and 'dead life'. 'Dead life' is that which inhabits a person who walks through life without sweating or urinating, and from whose body no foul substance emanates. For foulness, corruption, and rot are necessary corollaries of 'living life'. A living person cannot hold back the urine in his bladder indefinitely or he will die. Once he is dead, though, he can keep his foulness bottled up inside. He then becomes what might be called a 'clean corpse', in a scientific sense. From an artistic point of view, however, inner corruption is more deadly than foulness which is allowed to escape into the world outside. This is a well-known fact or phenomenon of nature, and it is for this reason that the smell of a dead body is much more foul than the odour of a body which is still alive.

I fancied (and my fancy, at that particular moment, amounted to fact) that one of the children who were circling round as they sang in unison suddenly moved outside of the circle. I saw the small body come loose from the steadily revolving ring, breaking the regularity of its outline. It moved off like a gleaming speck, or a star that has lost its eternal equilibrium, detached itself from the universe, and shot off at random, creating a trail of flame, like a shooting star just before it is consumed in its own fire.

With an instinctive curiosity, I followed his movement

with my gaze. He came to a stop so near to where I stood that I could see his face. It wasn't the face of a boy, as I had thought. No, it was the face of a little girl. But I wasn't absolutely certain, for children's faces – like those of old people – are sexless. It is in that phase between childhood and old age that gender must declare itself more openly.

The face – oddly enough – was not strange to me. So familiar was it, in fact, that it left me feeling bemused, and then my surprise turned to disbelief. My mind could not accept the sight before my eyes. It is just not plausible that, leaving home in the morning to go to work, on the way I should run head-on into another person only to discover that the face which met my gaze was none other than my own.

I confess that my body shook, and I was seized by a violent panic which paralysed my ability to think. Even so, I wondered: why should a person panic when he sees himself face to face? Was it the extreme weirdness of the situation in which I found myself, or was it the almost overwhelming familiarity of the encounter? At such a moment, one finds everything becoming utterly confused. Contradictory or incompatible things come to resemble each other so closely that they become almost identical. Black becomes white, and white turns to black. And the meaning of all this? One faces, with open eyes, the fact that one is blind.

I rubbed my eyes with trembling fingers, and looked at the child's face again, and again, any number of times. Perhaps I have been gazing into that face ever since. Maybe I am still looking at it, at this very moment, and at every moment, as if it is following me around as closely as my shadow, or clinging to me like a part of my body, like my own arm or leg.

Panic, by its nature, breeds loathing, and I cannot deny that I felt an instant hatred for this face. Some people might think I'm not speaking sincerely when I say this. Perhaps they will ask themselves how one can loathe his own face, or body, or any part of his body. No doubt those people have a point; after all, they're more able to see me than I am able to see myself. This is not a unique or personal tragedy: in fact, everyone suffers from it, for one is always most visible to others – whether frontally, in profile, or from the rear. While others know what we look like from behind, we can only look ourselves in the face – and that by means of a mirror.

The mirror is always at hand, positioned like another person standing between one and oneself. Even so, I have no animosity towards the mirror. As a matter of fact, I am practically in love with it. I adore gazing into it at length – staring into it, actually. I love to see my face. The truth is that I never tire of looking at my face, for it's a beautiful face, more beautiful than any other face I've ever seen on this earth. Moreover, every time I look at it, I discover new aspects of its beauty that almost bewitch me.

Not everyone will feel ill at ease with my frankness. But candour is not always welcome; in fact, it is rarely so. Nevertheless, I have promised myself to tell the truth. Speaking candidly is hard work, I know, and persisting in it requires ever-greater efforts and more and more sacrifices. One must give up trying to be attractive or acceptable at every moment; one must even accept that people may find a certain degree of ugliness in what we are or in what we say and do. Sometimes they may find us so ugly that we become repulsive to them. But this is the struggle demanded of freedom fighters, and also of anyone who wants to produce a good work of art, which is what I am trying to do.

What particularly dazzled me about this face were the eyes, and the eyes alone. Eyes are what I adore in a person most of all. And I believe (although my conviction may lack scientific foundation) that the eyes of a person are extremely sensitive organs, that in fact they are the most sensitive of all, followed

11

closely (and this is natural) by the reproductive organs. But what drew me most to the eyes was a certain light that seemed to shine in all directions, reflecting itself in all nooks and crannies, like the purest of fine-cut diamonds. It was certainly a confusing gaze, one that defied easy appraisal, for it wasn't a one-dimensional look with a clear meaning. It wasn't a look of sadness, or an expression of joy, a look of reproach or of fear. No, it was not a single look. It was a look composed of many looks, even if on the surface it seemed uniform. For soon enough the first look disappeared, to be followed by the second and third, each enveloped in turn, like the turning pages of a thick book or the folds of a length of fine weaving, successive layers piling themselves one atop the other.

My attention was so fully captured by the eyes that I noticed no other features of her face – neither nose, nor cheeks, nor lips – nor did I notice the tiny hand which rose in the air, waving to me with a gentle and familiar gesture as though she had known me all along.

'What's your name?' I asked her.
'Hamida.'
The voices of the children rose in unison, accompanied by their winding movement and circular song, circling ceaselessly so that one could not tell the beginning from the end.

Hamida had a baby,
She named him Abd el-Samad,
She left him by the canal bed,
The kite swooped down and snatched off his head!
Shoo! Shoo! Away with you!
O kite! O monkey snout!
Hamida had a baby . . .

I laughed, as adults normally do when they are trying to be playful with children.

'Are they singing for you?' I asked.

But I got no answer. She had vanished during the brief moment when my head moved as I laughed. I just barely caught a glimpse of her small back, bending slightly as she disappeared inside a dark wooden door on which was mounted a wooden human hand that served as a doorknocker.

I didn't bother with the doorknocker, as strangers to a household usually do when they are facing a closed door. I knew my way, despite the massed darkness that always squats in the entrances to these houses, a gloom made even heavier by the sun's setting long before. To my right, I saw the nanny-goat's head peeping out from behind the wall; to my left was a small step leading into a room, merely a slight elevation. Still, as I crossed it, I stumbled – just as I have every time – and almost fell on my face. I would have done, had it not been for my body's practised agility and its remarkable ability to regain a threatened balance.

I spotted her. She was lying on the reed mat, deep in sleep. Her eyelids were half closed, and her lips were parted just enough to let through the deep breaths of a sleeping child. Her arms were coiled around her head, and her right hand was closed over a penny or perhaps a halfpenny coin. Her long *gallabiyya** was hitched up over her thin, tender-skinned legs as far as the knees, and her little head quivered in a minute, hardly perceptible movement. Her small jaws were pressed lightly together, giving the impression of bliss dissolving in her mouth: a piece of candy, concealed beneath her tongue.

There was no moon, and the night was gloomy. The lamp, lit since early evening, had now become but a feeble wisp of light; either its wick had burnt out or the oil had been depleted. And as I stood there, a sudden, strong, hot gust of wind extinguished the faint tendril of light. The wind had burst in from the direction of the door, which actually wasn't a door at all, for the room possessed only that small, slightly raised threshold. But now that the lamp had gone completely out, the darkness had become so dense that one could not distinguish the floor from the walls, or the walls from the ceiling. Nothing at all was visible in the heavy blackness – nothing, that is, except a large object that filled the doorway completely, the only light now coming from two small round apertures set high in that wooden block, holes which emitted a piercing yellow light stained with the redness of still-glowing embers.

In that moment falling between the last threads of night and the first strands of day, not even the half-light which makes the way for dawn had emerged. In the darkness, his large, bare foot stumbled on the slight rise of the threshold. But his tall, broad body regained its balance, and he sprang forward, pantherlike, on tensile feet. He moved on, slowly and cautiously, stepping over something that looked very much like the backless leather slippers worn by men in the countryside.

Like the eyes of a wildcat whose sharp vision and sweeping night sight have not been tamed to dullness, those piercing, reddish-stained apertures made certain that she was on the mat. When his coarse, flattened fingers reached out to lift the *gallabiyya* from her pale thighs, she was still deep in sleep, enjoying the sound slumber of childhood. The dream, though, had shifted: the sweet had melted to nothing beneath her tongue, and the shopkeeper was demanding the penny. She opened her fingers; her hand was empty. The shopkeeper snatched up his stick and began to run after her.

As small and light as it was, her body could fly through the air like a sparrow. No doubt she would have been able to stay ahead of the shopkeeper (aah, had she only been a real sparrow!). But a feeling of heaviness came upon her, suddenly

14

and just the way it happens in dreams. She felt her body grow sluggish; it seemed to have turned into stone, into a statue whose feet are planted on the ground and whose arms are fixed in place with iron and cement. Her thighs, pulled apart, seemed to have turned into marble, and her legs, held stiffly in the air, were split wide open. The blows of the stick rained down between her thighs with a violence she had never known before.

She screamed, but no voice came out. A large, flat hand clapped down over her mouth and nose, stifling her. She became aware that a large body smelling of tobacco was pressing down onto her: this wasn't a dream, she realized. Although her eyes were nearly closed, she could make out the features of the face clearly enough to recognize their resemblance to those of her father or brother, one of her uncles or cousins, or another man – any man.

Like all children, when Hamida woke up each morning her mind was clear of the previous night's dreams. Sparrowlike, she would hop up from the mat and run to her mother with the happy cries of a child who greets the new day with a well-rested body and an empty stomach, eager for even a morsel of bread baked to such hardness that it can crack baby teeth, or a single gulp of milk straight from an udder, or a lump of old, fermented cheese scraped from the bottom of the clay jar.

That morning was no different from any other. But this dream had not been laid to rest, forgotten. Harsh fingers had left red and blue marks on her arms and legs, and she could still feel a pain between her thighs, while the aroma of tobacco clung to her skin.

Thinking it a fever, her mother bound Hamida's head in a kerchief and left her to lie on the mat. Hamida slept the entire day and through the night. She awoke the next morning believing the dream forgotten, as if it had evaporated in the air or been lost in the past, in fact as if it had never been. She

15

jumped up from the mat with her usual energy, except that she felt a slight heaviness in her legs which soon disappeared as she dressed for school and scampered off with the other children.

I could always distinguish Hamida from the rest, for her school pinafore was made of a coarsely woven, faded cream-coloured calico. Moreover, on the back was a stain that had been red a few days before, for as she sat in class, a spot of blood had seeped through her knickers. Her mother, who was always warning her to be ready for this event, had shown her how to put the rough cotton towel carefully between her thighs, for she was no longer a little girl. How often she had heard her mother's comment: 'I was your age when I got married – and my breasts weren't even showing yet.'

Whenever Hamida twisted around and saw the stain on the pinafore, she could feel the embarrassment beading her small, even forehead like sweat. She would dash home to take off the pinafore, replacing it with her *gallabiyya*. Squatting by the metal basin, she would wash out the garment, for it was her only school pinafore. Then she would hang it out on the line, in the sun, so that it would be dry before the next morning.

One day the pinafore became tight. Only with difficulty did she squeeze her body into it, especially from the front, over her belly. Bearing a strange expression that Hamida had never seen before, her mother's eyes came to rest on her belly. It was such a sombre, frightening look that it sent a light shiver through her small body. Her mother's large fingers closed around Hamida's skinny arm.

'Take off your pinafore!'

Hamida obeyed. She put on her *gallabiyya*, and huddled by the wall, finding a sunny patch in which to sit. Usually, her mother called her to lend a hand with the kneading or baking, or the cooking, or sweeping the house. Or her father, or one of her uncles, sent her to the shop to buy tobacco. One of her

16

aunts might hand over a still-nursing baby, to be cared for until she returned from working in the field. Or the neighbour would sing out from her rooftop, asking Hamida to fill her earthenware jar from the river. Her brother, or an uncle, would toss his dirty socks and pants at her for laundering. At sunset, the girls and boys of the neighbourhood would crowd around her. They would all scurry down to the street and play hide-and-seek, or cops and robbers, or 'the snake's gone, gone', or 'a grain of salt', or 'Hamida had a baby'.

But today, nothing of the sort happened. They left her alone, sitting in the sunshine. She couldn't find any way to pass the time except to stare at the path of the sun's disc across the sky. When it set, after a stretch of time, she remained there, sitting stolidly in the darkness, her small body trembling. She sensed something out of the ordinary, but didn't know what. Something dreadful was happening around her, in the darkness, in the dead silence, and in the eyes, everyone's eyes. Not even the chickens who were always about, crowding and pushing to get near her, approached as they normally did. The big black tomcat who usually came up to rub himself against her stopped at a distance and stared at her, his dilated eyes apprehensive, his long, sharply tapered ears held rigid.

Hamida's head drooped over her knees. She dozed off for a moment, or perhaps it was several hours later that she came to, suddenly conscious of long fingers taking hold of her arm. Alarmed, Hamida started, and would have screamed had it not been that her mother's hand was suddenly clapped over her mouth. Her mother's faint voice sounded more like a hiss:

'Come on, follow me, on your tiptoes.'

As there was no moon, and the half-light that just precedes the dawn had not yet appeared, the night was dark. The entire village was asleep, still and silent in that moment falling between the last hour of the night and the beginnings of day,

17

just before the dawn call to prayer. Her mother's large, bare feet almost ran over the dusty ground, with Hamida following so closely behind that she could almost touch the hem of her mother's gown.

She was just meaning to open her mouth to ask the question in her mind when her mother came to a halt at a squat wall which separated the main country road from the railroad. Hamida knew this wall: she often hid behind it when playing hide-and-seek. Her mother handed her a familiar-looking rectangle of black cloth: it was a *tarha*.

Hamida settled the *tarha* over her head so that it hung down over her body, covering her neck, shoulders, chest, back and belly. Now she looked just like one of the village women. As her mouth formed its question, the train whistle sent a shiver through her mother's body. A harsh tremor shook the ground beneath the woman's feet, and just as harshly her large fist plunged forward suddenly, pushing into her daughter's back, pushing Hamida towards the train. Again, her whispering voice was lowered almost to a hiss:

'The train doesn't wait for anyone. Go on, run away!'

Hamida leapt towards the approaching train, but then stopped to turn around momentarily. She saw her mother, standing exactly in the same place, as if rooted to the spot, impassive and motionless. The black *tarha* which enveloped her mother's head, shoulders and bosom was utterly still. Her chest showed not the slightest rise or fall, nor did any part of her show the tiniest movement. Even her eyelashes were frozen in place; she looked like a statue, a real one carved from stone.

The train was now coming into the station: a massive black head emitting smoke. The strong beam of its one large eye exposed the station. It also exposed Hamida, as she stood there out in the open. Hastily, she took cover behind a post. The train slowed, its cars colliding against each other, its iron

18

wheels screeching against the iron rails, producing such a loud and brazen sound as it came to a stop that Hamida thought the noise must have awakened everyone in the village. She rushed towards the train, pulling the edges of the *tarha* around her face to disguise herself as best she could.

She extended one small foot towards the steps leading up into the train. She had never ridden in a train before. There was a gap between platform and stairs, and her leg fell short. She pulled back her foot and glanced around in panic. She feared the train would start moving before she could manage to climb on. Seeing a throng of men and women boarding the forward carriage, she hurried over to stand behind them. She watched closely as, one after another, they ascended the steps. Every single one of them, she could see, took hold of an iron handle beside the doorway before placing a foot on the first step. She hadn't noticed that handle before. Hamida stuck out her right arm, clutched the handle as tightly as she could, pulled her body forward until her foot reached the step, and disappeared inside the carriage.

She sat down on the first seat that met her eyes, noticing that it was next to a window. As the train began to move slowly, she peered outside. She poked her head further out of the window. Her neck stiffened as she saw her mother, still standing in the same spot, impassive and motionless, everything frozen in place: *tarha*, head, chest, eyelashes, everything.

On the point of calling out, Hamida reminded herself that it was no longer her mother whom she could see, but rather the statue of the peasant woman that had stood at the entrance to the village for many years – how many she did not know. She could not remember a time when she had not seen it there. It must have been there forever; it must have been there even before she was born.

Her head still outside the window, she regained her breath in a few gasps. It was the first time she had experienced the feel of tears on her face or their taste in her mouth. But she did not move, not even to wipe off her tears on the sleeve or hem of her *gallabiyya*. She let them run down her face, and when they reached the inner corner of her mouth, she licked them off without visibly moving a single facial muscle. She didn't make a sound or flicker an eyelid; not even her eyelashes trembled. Everything had gone pitch black. The train dissolved into the blackness and blended into the night, like a drop melting into the depths of the sea.

* * * * *

As Hamida's train pulled away, Hamido was still lying inert on the reed mat. Although his eyes were closed in sleep, he could see his father's eyes in the faint light. His father stood tall and straight, like the trunk of a eucalyptus tree which has sent its roots deep into the earth.

An oppressive chill ran through Hamido's small body, numbing his arms and legs as if he were caught in a troublesome dream. He lay motionless, his steady gaze directed at that tall, impassive phantom. Somehow, he knew that something serious had happened, or soon would. He held his breath and vanished completely under the grimy, blackened coverlet, his small fingers pulling it taut around his head. His right ear, atop the hard pillow, trembled in time to the beating of his heart, which seemed to issue from his head rather than his chest.

At any moment he expected those long fingers to reach out and strip off the bedcover, exposing his head. The wide-open eyes would settle their gaze on his, filling his eyes with whatever it was that was so ominous. But the coverlet remained in place, pulled tightly over his head. In the silence he could hear his own heartbeat resound in the room. And despite the darkness, he could see the movement of his chest,

20

so slight as to be almost invisible, like the ever-so delicate stirring of treetops on a still and moonless night, unrelieved by a single breath of moving air; when the darkness, like his grimy bedcover, has wrapped itself over sky and earth, in that brief moment hidden on the boundary of night and day, before the threads of dawn begin to appear and the darkness creeps away. The gloom lifts slowly, like a huge fish swimming in an endless ocean where lie the village's small mud huts, huddled together in the depths like a huge heap of black dung.

When Hamido opened his eyes, daylight already filled the room. What he had seen was nothing but a dream; he was absolutely sure of it. He jumped up from the mat and ran out into the street. His friends, children of the neighbouring families, were playing as usual in the narrow lane extending along and between the mud-brick façades. Each child held fast to the hem of the next one's *gallabiyya*, forming a dancing, whistling, train. Then they would break apart and play hide-and-seek, concealing themselves behind the dung heaps, inside the animal pens, behind a large earthenware water jar inside one of the houses, or inside the mouth of an oven.

He saw Hamida amongst the children, running for cover behind a pile of dung. She squatted so that her head would not show above the mound. But he could see her white thighs, and between them a thin strip of rough brown calico. Even though she attempted to hide her crop of soft black hair in the dust so that no one would see her, Hamido spotted her at once. This time, he was the seeker, so he bounded off at a run, his bare feet stirring up a whirlwind of dust as he headed towards her.

He fixed his eyes on the dung heap, pretending not to see her. He advanced on tiptoe, slowly, cautiously, and swerved as if to conceal himself behind the heap. Then he sprang – a single jump, a panther's leap – and grabbed her by the hair. His other hand shot out with lightning speed and he let it rest on her thigh for a few moments. Then his small, stiff fingers

21

pulled at her knickers, but Hamida kicked and butted him, as she did whenever the seeker caught her. She managed to free herself of his grasp, and ran to hide behind another dung heap.

Hamida was not the only one to play hide-and-seek, for all the village children joined in the game. When any of the girls ran to hide, and squatted to conceal themselves, their small white thighs were bared and their cheap, dirty knickers showed, looking like thin black strips between their thighs. The seeker – whoever it was – would grab at the strip, trying to pull the knickers down. But the girl knew how to aim a practised kick, with one or both feet. The seeker would not give in either, but would fight her with the same methods. A battle in miniature would ensue, an almost imperceptible skirmish, for the dung heap concealed the pair of small bodies. But four tender, little feet could be seen, jutting out from behind the pile, the girl's foot indistinguishable from the boy's: in childhood, feet – like faces – are sexless, especially if the feet are bare, for only shoes define their gender.

Her kick propelled Hamido backwards, and he toppled over on to his behind. He recovered quickly, though, and so did she; as he got to his feet, he caught sight of her face. It wasn't Hamida. His eyes swept the area, peering at all the children in turn. He ran to the house to search for her – in the animal pen, in the mouth of the oven, behind the water jar, under the mat. He came out of the house at a run, looking for her – behind the dung heaps, behind the tree trunk, shimmying up the date-palm, under the embankment of the village's irrigation canal. Daytime slipped away, night began to fall, and still he had found no trace of her.

He paused on the canal embankment, peering into the gloom. His solitary shadow was reflected on the surface of the sluggish, mud-laced water. The shadow was that of a child, but his face no longer bore any resemblance to the smooth, soft, sexless faces of children. Had the water's surface been clear,

22

with the tranquil purity of fresh water, perhaps it would have yielded an unclouded mirror and reflected his face to better advantage. Like all irrigation channels, however, this canal eddied with mud, its slow-moving surface obstinately pursuing a zigzagging course, meandering and twisting into wrinkles like the skin of an ancient face.

His eyes seemed to have widened and aged, as he stared fixedly, impassively, into the darkness, not blinking once, even his eyelashes frozen in place. For the first time, a large tear lay motionless on the surface of his eye. Before, his tears had always been children's tears, moving constantly, flickering with the fitful light of glimmery stars. In childhood, the flicker of tears and the flicker of smiles blend into one and the same glimmer.

But no one would have made a mistake at that particular moment. It was Hamido who stood with his body planted on the canal embankment. It was not a child, and this large tear was not the tear of a child. It was a real tear, tangible as it rolled over the face, and salty as it crept into the mouth.

This was real salt, for tears, like all body fluids, contain salt. And Hamido did not know how live without Hamida, for she was no ordinary sister. Hamida was his twin. And there are two types of twins, those who develop from two embryos living in one womb, and those who grow from a single embryo which produces male and female. Hamido and Hamida had been one embryo, growing inside one womb. From the beginning they had been one cell, a single entity. Then everything split into two, even the tiniest features, even the minute, tiny muscle under each eye. No longer could anyone distinguish Hamido from Hamida. Even their mother used to confuse them.

But Hamido knew he was something other than Hamida. He was aware that ever since their birth his body had been separate from hers. The resemblance was strong, though, and

23

it was so easy to mix them up that sometimes he himself became confused and thought he was Hamida. Concealing himself behind a wall, he would raise his *gallabiyya* until he could peer between his thighs. When his eyes fell on that small, narrow cleft, he thought himself Hamida; then, a stick held tightly in a huge hand would swing down over his head, causing him to pull his *gallabiyya* hastily down over his body and cry. His tears, though always real, vanished quickly as children's tears do. Spotting the stick that had been tossed on the ground, he would scurry over and pick it up, jamming it into the deep pocket of his *gallabiyya*. From time to time, he would reach into his pocket to finger it. Its hardness penetrated his fingers and moved on, into his arm, his shoulder, his neck, and when he tightened his neck muscles, his head would be thrown back, repeating the movement his father was wont to make with his head. He would try to speak from his throat, producing a coarse, oppressive timbre that echoed his father's voice.

Whenever Hamida heard her brother speak with his rough intonation she knew that the stick was in his possession. She couldn't see it, of course, but knowing he had it hidden somewhere beneath his *gallabiyya*, she would take flight, Hamido following at a run. To the casual observer, they would seem to be at play, but Hamido was not a child, and he had something hidden in his *gallabiyya* pocket, something hard which hung down his thigh like an alien limb.

And should Hamida glance in his direction and see his face, she would not know that it was Hamido standing there. The surprise would stop her in her tracks – or perhaps it was fright that caused her to freeze on the spot, as if she were a statue. Hamido's open palm would move over the sculptured surface, touching the stony eyelids, and poking a finger between eyelid and eye, just like any child exploring the head of a new doll – especially one of those big ones with hair and

24

eyelashes so real that it could almost be alive.

Never in his life had Hamido held a doll, whether large or small. Peasant children don't play with shop-bought dolls, or rag dolls made at home, or toy trains, or paper boats, or balls, or anything else. In fact, they don't know what playing is. After all, playing is for children, which they are not. They are born full-grown, like insect larvae, who no sooner know the touch of the earth than they fly, or like the worms which reproduce and grow in fermented cheese: as soon as the new worm separates from its mother, one can hardly tell the young worm from the old one.

Hamido caught sight of Hamida's face; as she walked towards him from afar along the canal embankment, his heart pounded with the primal joy of children. But as she drew nearer, he recognized his mother's black *tarha*, encircling her head and falling over her body. He ran to her and rested his head against her belly: when Hamido stood tall next to his mother, his head came up no further than her waist. He filled his nostrils with his mother's distinctive smell, blending into the odours of bread baking, the soil of the fields, and sycamore figs. He loved sycamore figs. Whenever he spotted his mother returning from the fields, sycamore fruits wrapped in her *tarha*, he would run to her. Seating herself beside him on the ground, she would give him the figs, one by one, after blowing the dust from them.

His mother pushed him away with one hand. But he pressed himself against her, stubbornly clinging to her body and managing to insert his head beneath her left breast. It was precisely here that he loved to rest his head when sleeping next to her at night. Although she would position herself on the other edge of the mat, at a distance from him, he habitually awoke in the middle of the night, and, not seeing her beside him, would crawl over and bury his head under her breast.

She did not always push him away. Sometimes, her arms

came out and encircled him, pressing him to her so fiercely that she would hurt him. Through him would run a mysterious, vague feeling that she was not his mother – nor was she an aunt, nor any relation at all – but rather a stranger, her body alien to his. He would feel an unfamiliarity that made him shiver, generating a tremor that ran from surface to depths, convulsing his body like the shivering of a fever.

The tremor shook him so violently that he wrapped his arms around her, but he felt her big strong hand – strong as his father's – pushing him away, pushing him so forcefully that he nearly fell into the embankment's waiting grasp. He lifted his face to look at her, and saw instead the ageing, dilated eyes of his father, red capillaries running over their white expanse. His shivering grew more violent; he was so scared that he opened his mouth to let out a scream, but was prevented by his father's great hand, clapped over his mouth, and his father's coarse voice that now sounded more like a hiss:

'Follow me.'

As there was no room, and the half-light which just precedes the dawn had not yet appeared, the night was dark. The entire village was asleep, still and silent in that moment falling between the last hour of the night and the beginnings of day, just before the dawn call to prayer. His father's large, bare feet practically ran over the dusty ground, with Hamido following so closely behind that he could almost touch the hem of his father's robe.

He was just meaning to open his mouth to ask the question in his mind when his father came to a halt at a squat wall which separated the main country road from the railroad. Hamido knew this wall: he often hid behind it when playing hide-and-seek. His father handed him a long object, rigid and sharp, which gleamed in the darkness like a knife.

Hamido jammed the knife into his *gallabiyya*, and it fell deep into his pocket, where it hung down alongside his thigh.

He felt its sharp, pointed tip against his flesh; the muscles of his thighs, legs, and feet contracted, and he stood rooted to the ground. The piercing sound of the train whistle made the ground beneath him shake, so that he had to plant his feet even more firmly on the ground, resisting any movement, as if he were an intractable wild horse. But his father's large, powerful hand pushed into his back, and his coarse voice, kept low, came out once again like a hiss:

'Only blood washes out shame. Go on, follow her!'

So Hamido plunged towards the approaching train, but then stopped to turn around momentarily. He spotted his father, standing exactly in the same place as before, as if rooted to the ground, impassive and motionless, eyelids unmoving, the capillaries on the whites of his eyes frozen in place, like threads of blood drawn on a painting with a careful hand.

* * * * *

Just as her brother boarded the train, Hamida was stepping down on to the station platform. It seemed as if she were sinking into an ocean, a turbulent sea with waves not of water but of humanity: men, women, and children, all wearing sturdy leather shoes. And long lines of cars, that to Hamida looked like trains, went by in a steady stream, moving along gleaming streets that showed no dirt, branching out in all directions only to intertwine and then diverge once more, endlessly, like a tree sending its crown high into the heavens and plunging its roots deep into the earth. And the houses here were packed together in a single, enormous, towering mass that entirely obscured the sky. The commotion, the sounds of people and car horns, were deafening, and Hamida could no longer hear a thing. But her bare feet were moving over the asphalt as if of their own accord, one foot behind the other, in that natural movement one learns from earliest childhood. As

27

she did not know her way, Hamida might have gone on in this mechanical fashion indefinitely. She had no idea where her path had started, or whence it might take her. But her movements were interrupted by a heavy leather shoe that trod on her left foot and almost crushed it. She staggered back momentarily, only to find an enormous car bearing down on her. Her mouth open to its widest, Hamida shrieked; her voice, stifled for so long, let go in a long, shrill scream which lasted as long as two or three normal screams, or ten or a hundred or a thousand successive screams all merging into a single, unbroken sound that went on and on as though it would continue for all time.

The terrific din swallowed up her scream as the waves of the sea swallow a drop of water, a bit of straw, a butterfly, or a newborn bird not yet able to fly. No one heard her voice, and her scream changed nothing. Around her, the world surged on, like a roaring cataract that tears apart crocodiles and leaves the splintered remains of ships in its wake, its pulverizing waters unaffected all the while, and its surface remaining as white as ever.

Hamida hobbled on her wounded foot to a sheltered corner next to a wall that seemed relatively remote from both vehicles and people. She leant her head back against the wall and stared before her, into the hazy vagueness that seemed to envelop everything around her, as if she were engulfed in a dream – or a nightmare – from which she would awaken shortly, to jump up from the mat like a little bird. She made to support her weight on her hand in order to spring up. But her palm brushed against her belly, and suddenly the haze lifted. Things fell into place, becoming intelligible not through the rational faculty which takes in new facts, but with that instinctive, mysterious understanding which issues from an utterly fatigued body in moments of rest or extreme languor.

She fell asleep right where she was, and awoke hungry. She

noticed a bakery just next to the spot she had chosen, and out in front – very near indeed – sat row after row of carefully arranged loaves. She reached out a skinny arm; her fingers closed around a loaf and brought it to her mouth. She was just closing her teeth on it when a large hand gripped her arm.

She inhaled sharply, her chest rising up so that her small breasts showed, just like two olives, beneath the wide-cut gallabiyya; her protruding belly, inflated like a child's balloon, revealed itself too. The black tarha still covered her head and hair and fell over her shoulders as far as her lower back, coming to an end just above her small, rounded buttocks.

Her gaze travelled upwards in alarm until they met a pair of eyes staring straight at her. She tugged at the tarha, bringing it across to half-hide her face, as she had seen the women of her village do. Only a single eye was visible now, dilated and black, its look of bafflement still alight with the innocent sparkle of childhood: the gleam of an eye that had always been closed, and was now opening for the first time on to the infinite world. A taut, circular muscle – like a severed question mark – surrounding the eye intimated alarm, and over the cornea dry tears had deposited a film which hung there like a light cloud. She sensed a new feeling creeping over her face, moving from the bridge of her nose towards one eye: a realization that she was a female, with a femininity not yet complete. No one had acquainted her with herself; it was she who had discovered this, on her own, a few minutes before, finding herself to be a newly ripening fruit, fresh and still coated with dew.

Eluding the large hand, she managed to slip off at a run. The figure charged behind her. She turned into a street and hid behind one of its many doors. Poking her head out, she saw no one there and believed herself safe. But the long arm appeared from somewhere behind her and grabbed her by the neck, and a rough, brutal voice pierced her ears.

'I've got you now, thief! You're under arrest! Come on, now, walk ahead of me, to the police station!'

She gave in, leaving her thin white arm to his grasp. The hand clutching her was coarse and large, its joints protruding and its bones unnaturally curved, with veins bulging beneath the skin. Under the stubby fingernails ran a layer of dirty black. Her eyes crept up the long arm: over each broad shoulder marched a horizontal row of five brass buttons, separated by a burly neck encased in a high collar blackened around the inner rim with dirt dissolved in sweat. The collar encircled his neck with perfect fit, then descended over his chest in a line of ten brass buttons. During her stretch of compulsory schooling, Hamida had learnt some rudiments of arithmetic, and she began counting the buttons. Five over each shoulder, that makes ten on the shoulders, plus ten more on the chest: that makes twenty buttons in all.

Midday had arrived, and the sun was now blazing hot. Its red disc was reflected in the round brass buttons, giving them the likeness of twenty suns that made one's eyes water at a mere glance. Unable to go on looking at them, she dropped her gaze to the ground. But the surface beneath her bare feet seemed aflame; she had never felt such heat underfoot before. His high boots struck the ground with a strange metallic sound, like iron grating against iron. His stride was long, each foot planting itself firmly on the asphalt. The feet rose into long legs inside trousers of heavy cloth, with a deep, vault-like pocket in which was hiding a sharp, hard implement, hanging down along his thigh.

They turned off the broad thoroughfare into a narrow side street, the long fingers still encircling her arm. But now the five fingers had become only four. The fifth had disengaged itself from the rest, moving upwards on its own, over the soft arm, cautiously, stealthily, until it buried its coarse black tip into the soft childlike armpit that as yet bore no sign of hair.

30

She tried to pull her arm away. But the four fingers contracted, closing around her upper arm more tightly, digging into the soft flesh, while the fifth finger emerged from beneath her armpit, straining until its pointed black snout reached as far as the soft rise of her breast – still just a bud – bearing down on it with cautious, trembling, jerky pressure which became firmer at the bend of a street, or behind a wall, and relaxing or stopping altogether whenever they were walking down the middle of the street; and occasionally, as they passed a throng of people, that fifth finger would retract itself quickly and join its four brothers.

A foul odour suddenly filled her nostrils; she found herself in a dark, narrow alley. She saw him come to a stop before a small wooden door. He drew a key from his pocket, unlocked the door, pushed her inside ahead of him, and closed the door.

At first she could see nothing, for the place was pitch dark. He lit a small kerosene lamp, which at once revealed a bare, tiled floor, with just a little rug in one corner that reminded her of the mat at home. It was a cramped room, and had only a single, small, iron-barred window high in the wall, a clay water-jug perching on its sill. In the faint light, the walls of the room looked a grey colour, overlaid with the sort of black tint produced by soot from a gas burner. On a nail in the wall hung a suit of heavy cloth. From its chest and broad, padded shoulders, yellow brass buttons gleamed in the darkness like eyes, open and feverish with a viral liver infection. On the floor sat one huge, high-topped boot, looking like a headless animal, and beside it was tossed a pair of white, baggy pants, the rear yellowed and the belly gone blackish, giving off the smell of old urine.

She raised her head from the tiled floor and saw him standing there, naked. His broad shoulders had become narrow – bony, even – and his collarbone protruded sharply. The sturdy trouser legs had given way to thin and bowed

31

limbs; his massive feet, which before had rested so far above the ground, now had nothing to separate them from the tiles. The sharp, rigid implement concealed in his pocket had become visible.

She caught her breath with a gulp, her surprise imbued with a panic that she resisted instinctively. But he threw her down on the floor, his bulky finger tearing at the neck of her *gallabiyya* so that the threadbare garment ripped in half down the front, revealing no underclothes below.

'Who are you?' she asked, her voice cracked and weak.

'I'm the government.'

'The Lord keep you – let me go.'

He answered in the same coarse, imperious tones. 'Go where, girl? You're already condemned.'

Everything began to happen with the extreme rapidity of panting breaths, of muscles contracting and expanding, an extraordinary speed which occurs only in dreams. But this time no confusion marked the dream: instead of a shopkeeper beating her with his stick, there was before her a male creature with a rough moustache that rubbed coarsely across her face, a smell of tobacco which stifled her, and a chest of thick hair, matted and plastered to the skin by a sticky, viscous sweat.

Suddenly everything stopped: a moment of stillness akin to the moment of death. She lifted her head from the tiled floor and looked about her. She saw him lying on his back, eyes closed, utterly still. She thought perhaps he had died, when a faint snore began to issue from his gaping mouth, soon rising to become like the gurgling of an ancient waterwheel turned by an ailing bull. She raised herself quietly and composedly from the floor, pulled the two sections of her torn *gallabiyya* over her chest and stomach as best she could, and tiptoed to the door. She twisted her head back calmly, and saw the twenty yellow eyes, wide open and staring at her. Hastily, she opened the door.

32

The broad main street was visible ahead of her. She took off along it, running with all the strength she could summon, fleeing without a moment's pause.

*   *   *   *   *

That very moment, Hamido had stepped down from the train. Now, his back to the south and his face turned northward, he stared straight ahead, gazing at the many faces crowding the area outside the Bab al-Hadid railway station, Cairo's old central depot. His bare feet padded over the asphalt; beneath the ample folds of his *gallabiyya*, the knife swung down close to his thigh like an artificial limb or an organ newly implanted in his flesh.

The knife's sharp tip bumped against the flesh of his thigh, and he shivered, the tremor passing through his neck and head. He staggered, and almost fell among the heavy leather shoes surrounding him, but he tautened his leg muscles and kept his balance. His eyes lost themselves in the vast, buffeting ocean: rising with the buildings' towering summits, falling with the sun's rays reflected on the gleaming asphalt, circling with the movement in the immense traffic circle, at the centre of which stood a huge stone statue with a human head. Around it moved row after row of people, and flags, and cars, round and round, uncoiling and branching off into numerous straight lines, only to intertwine once again, pouring into another traffic circle, and then branching off, the branches splitting into still more branches, separating, then mingling again, and dividing, endlessly.

He shaded his eyes with his hands and leant his head back against a lamp-post. He couldn't fight the drowsiness which was overwhelming him, and he dozed off standing up. A muted sound awakened him. Glancing around, he noticed that the boulevard, submerged in the evening gloom, was now calm and empty of people and vehicles. His sharp eyes bored into the darkness, and he caught sight of a spectre running in the distance, its feet bare, its long *gallabiyya* not loose enough to hide the visible swelling over the stomach.

'Hamida!' He gasped her name out, sending a rush of pent-up breath through his barely parted lips, then took off over the asphalt, his left hand raised protectively before him, slashing at the darkness, and his right hand plunged into his pocket, fingering the sharp hardness of the knifeblade. The spectre stopped in a darkened corner. With slow, wary footsteps, Hamido drew nearer, until there was no more than a single stride between them. He heard the rough voice, coming in a whisper that was more like a hiss.

'Only blood washes out shame.'

He pulled the weapon from his pocket and hid it behind his back. Suddenly, a moving searchlight exposed the darkened corner, and he saw his mother's face beneath the black *tarha*. He screamed; the sound rang out in the night and the light came to a stop on his face. Someone drew near; in the darkness, he couldn't see the figure's eyes. But he could see eyes on the shoulders and over the chest – two rows of eyes, round and staring, giving off a yellowish light.

His lips formed their question, but a large, coarse palm landed on his temple, followed by a second slap across the other temple. He lifted his arm to resist the blows, but it was arrested by five tightly encircling fingers. He brought his other arm upwards instinctively protecting himself, when there loomed in the air a cudgel-like wooden arm that came down on his head.

Hamido opened his eyes to a violent headache. Probing his head, amidst the hair he stumbled on the wound, already crusted over with dry blood. He scratched at the scab until it fell, landing beside a huge pair of boots rising to high leather tops, surrounded by a trouser-fold of heavy cloth. The legs

34

seemed awesomely long; he realized they stretched up eventually into a stocky chest. Down the front and across the shoulders were fixed two rows of round yellow buttons which reflected a faint lamplight.

The enormous boot trod on the clot of dried blood, trampling it brutally underfoot. With the thud of the boot on the floor, there rose in the air a harsh voice.

'Your name?'

'Hamido.'

The sharp razor passed across the skin of his head: his thick hair tumbled into a pail, along with his *gallabiyya*. The sun of early morning was slanting in, and he saw the shadow of a tall, broad-shouldered person following him across the floor. The shadow came to a stop. He moved; it moved. He struck the floor with his foot and heard a strange metallic sound, not one that he had ever heard his own, bare, foot make. He looked at his feet, and there he saw the enormous, heavy boots, rising into high leather tops. He saw trousers of heavy cloth. Inside trousers and boots were his very own, actual, skinny legs, which extended upwards into a broad squarish chest, bolted with a row of brass buttons, and then into broad shoulders padded with cotton, or perhaps with straw.

In his new boots, he paced the ground, taking slow, timorous steps. Inside each boot rested a small, bony foot, clenched and compressed under the thick leather, its toes thin and white, bloodless and motionless, dead or nearly so, the entire foot absolutely still inside the boot. It was the boots which gave movement to those feet, lifting and lowering them, carrying them over the ground step by step. With every step over the asphalt, the iron-studded soles produced a dull thud, metallic and slow, like the sound made by the hoof of a sickly calf as it is driven to the slaughterhouse.

He stopped; so did the black shadow, sketched so meticulously on the ground. The utter smoothness of his

35

shaven head reflected the sun, and his eyes were no more than holes emitting a penetrating light. His neck muscles were stretched taut and his back muscles tensed; beneath the tight wall of his abdomen lay a distended emaciated stomach, fed only on black smoke, black saliva, and an end of dry bread, baked to hardness, which he dipped in treacle and ate with a slice of onion, or a bit of pickle which stung like a bitter cucumber, to balance out the sweet taste of the treacle. Then he would neutralize the bitterness with black smoke, sucked in through nose, mouth, and gullet to fill his chest and create pressure on his stomach until he could belch like one whose belly is full.

A thin whip stung him on the nape of his neck; his feet moved automatically over the ground. Right foot first, then left foot – iron cleats thudding against asphalt with a regular beat, like the hour striking or the heart beating, lub dub lub dub. Left right left right.

'Halt!' The strong, harsh voice resounded through the air. The boots on his feet collided against each other noisily. His legs and thighs came together tightly, muscles contracted. His right hand plunged into his pocket and came to rest over the killing tool, its hardness extending along his thigh and ending in a tapered and punctured metal head.

'Attention!' shouted that grating voice.

The fingers of his right hand closed around the implement – four fingers only, the thumb moving away to rest alone over the hammer. He had one eye trained on the fixed point halfway between the open eyes.

His mouth dropped open and he began to pant. But a strong hand slapped him across the stomach, and the harsh voice pierced his ear.

'Close your mouth. Hold your breath.'

He obeyed. The rough, commanding voice sounded.

'Only blood washes out shame!'

36

And he pulled the trigger.

He heard a loud report, a sound he had never heard before, and saw a body fall to the ground. From beneath it ran a red stream which he recognized at once as ewe's blood. For today was the feast-day, and here he was, still upright, his stance unchanged, staring at the pair of open eyes, still and lidless eyes, fixed in a cold, dead stare, eyes that had dilated with terror. The terror shifted to him; beneath the full *gallabiyya* his thin legs began to shake, and he ran to bury his head in his mother's bosom and weep.

He rubbed his face against his mother's chest, wiping away his tears. He looked up. There were his father's eyes, covered with the tiny red capillaries. There were the brass buttons over the chest and shoulders, with their own unique gleam, and the hoarse voice, with its frightening, peremptory harshness.

'Crying like a woman, hunh?'

And Hamido returned to his position in the rank. He stood erect, his eyes reflecting the redness of the sun directly overhead – for their blackness had fled, beneath the lid, under the shade, to a secure and moist place. The asphalt blazed, and seemed to melt in the heavy heat. He felt that the heels of his boots were digging into the asphalt, in the way that they would bore into the soft, muddy ground.

Hamido stopped for a second to pull up his boot tops. Lagging one step behind his row, he felt the stinging blow of the whip on his nape, and bounded forward to get in line. But instead he tripped and fell on his face.

His boots slipped off just as he was toppling over. The burning air thrust its way into his chest in the shape of a spoken word, uttered in a voice that he realized was his own. He became aware that it was his own body, and no one else's, that had fallen to the ground, and that the regular beats pounding on his inner ear were in fact issuing from his own chest. He felt proud of his ability to distinguish his body from that of the ewe.

Pride showed in his eyes, although his face was still to the ground. Spittle flew from the coarse mouth, coming to rest on the back of his head. And it was followed immediately by a familiar curse – an epithet pertaining to female genitalia – and then by a fierce kick with the blunt toe of a heavy boot, which landed in his back, directly over his kidney.

This sort of kick with the hard snout of a boot did not carry the same force every time, though, for I used to see Hamido clambering to his feet afterwards and running to join his rank. But today was the feast-day. And the big chief – his master – was to attend the celebrations in person, not through a delegate, as he usually did. Naturally, any mistake whatsoever – even a slight misstep – would be unforgiveable. On this particular day, a slip of the foot was not a mere slip of the foot, but rather was immediately transformed into something else, something far more serious. A misstep would distort the rank. And when one rank gets out of order, naturally the others become misshapen too. And this spells disaster right through.

Thus, everything went awry, becoming blurred and jumbled before Hamido's eyes. This was due not only to a deficiency in his powers of observation, but also to a lack of time. For, on such an important day as this, time is limited indeed, and the pace of life quickens to become a series of gasps. No one is able to breathe naturally, for everyone must gasp for breath if things are to remain as they should.

Like everyone else, then, Hamido panted, and as he did so a certain eye caught sight of him. Somewhere in the vicinity, there is always an eye which takes notice of whatever is going on. Observing things, staring with uninhibited intrusiveness into the lives – or deaths – of others, it gives the living no space to enjoy life, nor the dead respite in which to enjoy death. Hamido brought his legs together with a rather shy and fumbling movement (for meanwhile he had acquired a certain amount of diffidence) clearing the way for the procession of vehicles. But since time was so short, his right leg had no time to draw back as it should have, quickly; extended into the road, barefoot, his stiff toes quivering visibly, there it was in full sight of everyone.

Baffled, the procession stopped before this unprecedented and never-to-be-repeated scene. For the history books make no mention of any such incident of this type. Yet perhaps this is not so surprising, for what is recorded as history and what actually occurs in real life are two different things. And in this particular case, what actually occurred was so momentous that it deserved to find a place in history. But, being what it is, history does not open its pages to the recording of momentous events – especially if their hero is Hamido.

Hamido did not feel that he was a hero, despite the crowd which gathered around him: for in no time, an overwhelming number of people had collected. The empty spaces between buildings filled up with bodies; heads obstructed doors and windows; people left their offices and bureaus, and locked their shops, crowding into tightly compressed rows to enjoy the spectacle. I don't think anyone lagged behind – whether little or big, male or female, upper class or lower class – for all wanted to amuse themselves. To seek pleasure is, after all, a universal pastime, and legitimate on condition that it takes place in secret.

Hamido was still on the ground, in the same position, his eyes closed; for death, of course, has its effects. Even so, he saw lots and lots of men around him (for the vision of the dead is sharper than that of the living). He knew they were men by their shaved heads, the rubbery tubing and brass buttons on their uniforms, and of course by the hard killing tools hanging down alongside their thighs.

He tried to open his mouth to defend himself, to tell his

39

story, beginning it with the day his mother gave birth to him. But the big chief – his master – was present, and in his presence time is restricted. There isn't time enough for anyone. In any case, it is in the nature of things that the judgement must be issued first, and signed or imprinted with the thumbprint or sign of the accused to show that he is aware of its contents. Furthermore, the accused must follow the directives spelled out in the ruling. Only after all of this has been done will there be sufficient time for anything else – such as an appeal in which the condemned can claim innocence.

Thus, with all due promptness, Hamido's sentence was issued. In fact, it filled up an entire page of the official register. The law specified that Hamido must read the police report before putting his signature or thumbprint to it, for this would indicate his compliance with the contents. The words were unclear and not easy to read though, for the handwriting was poor and the report had been written in great haste. Hamido had difficulty making out the script, especially since he had not learnt to read or write, but he was able to pick out a word or two in each line. It amazed him that the police had shown such an ability to transform him from an unknown soldier into a hero – even if his heroism was so far outside the norms governing these things that wiggling his bare toes in his big chief's face had come to be considered, in his case, as a gesture of rebellion. Hamido was no longer able to contain or conceal his pride, and he began wiggling his toes, with slow and dignified movements that were full of an almost regal self-esteem.

All those present raised their hands to applaud – including the big chief, his master, who was in the front row. (The movements of the big chief, like the movement of history, cannot afford to ignore the masses.) And when his arms swung upward to applaud, the sandwich stuffed with ewe's meat, which he had concealed under his arm, fell to the ground. A lame child who was crawling among the crowded rows of people, carrying small sacks of toasted seeds for sale, snatched the sandwich away immediately.

Hamido smiled, even though he understood nothing of what was happening around him. The scene had not been intentional; he could take no credit for it. Moreover, it had been imperfectly executed, showing a lack of experience, and deficient in the requisite cultural background and perusal of The Heritage. Hamido had not read the many volumes pertaining to our Cultural Heritage; specifically and most significantly, he had not studied the tales of platonic love, derived from the era when love was clean and pure and people were honourable, back in those days when their sex organs had not yet been created.

But then Adam had committed The Great Crime (as Hamido's mother had told him), and lo and behold, there appeared an ugly organ growing between his thighs. It was a divine revenge – a just one, according to Hamido's mother. At this point in his musings, a question occurred to him that had never come to his mind before (perhaps because his body was now dead, and thus he could give his soul the right to think of sacred subjects). That question was the following: how had Adam committed the crime before this organ had been created for him?

Hamido made an attempt to rid himself of this speculation, for thinking about such matters could only be considered an immoral practice, especially in the presence of the big chief, his master. Hamido stole a quick glance between his thighs, but did not find the member in question. Instead, and in its place, he found a small cleft which reminded him of the cleft he used to see on Hamida's body. He thought there must be some mistake: perhaps the bodies of the dead had been confused, and in the final sorting they had given him a woman's body. Mistakes are bound to occur in the final

41

sorting: the civil servant who is responsible for the procedure has poor eyesight due to pulmonary tuberculosis. To make matters worse, he is the only one assigned to this task. (The budget doesn't allow for any expansion in personnel.) This civil servant is charged with transferring names from the initial to the final sorting lists. But the letters of some names are similar, particularly as certain names given to females can be distinguished from male names only by the single-letter, feminine ending: Amin becomes Amina, Zuhayr turns into Zuhayra, Mufid goes to Mufida, and Hamido becomes Hamida. In other words, with a mere stroke of the pen, man becomes woman.

Sometimes, Hamido loved being a woman, while at other times he resisted it strongly. For in those days women were charged with certain humiliating tasks normally performed by servants, like wiping a man's shoes when he came out of the lavatory, or giving him a glass of water as he lay on his back belching out loud (and belching out loud was the prerogative solely of men) or washing out his smelly socks or his underpants, which were even smellier because of the urine and the short supply of soap and water.

Hamido did try to rectify the situation. But this was not easy even in the best of circumstances, since he always had to establish that he was *not* a woman. Every time, they summoned the medical examiner, who would strip off Hamido's soiled pants with grumbling displeasure and look between his thighs, insolently. Sometimes, the examiner would not verify it simply by looking, but would insist on extending his elegant hand, with its carefully pruned nails, to examine the shrivelled and terror-stricken member. Measuring it from all angles with a finely calibrated plastic ruler, he would then take out his Parker fountain-pen and record the numbers in a notebook specifically designated for this purpose. He despatched these numbers inside an envelope sealed with red wax to the police's Department of Citizen Identification and Documentation.

Now, in this department reigned complete bedlam. Fingerprints were confused with footprints, and both with prints of other parts of the body. First and last digits were mixed up; portions of numbers were dropped and misplaced, while other portions were blotted out. This was due to the bad quality of the ink, for it was adulterated (corruption was widespread at that time: an entire bucket of water might well be added to a bottle of ink).

As a result, and in this fashion, Hamido's status remained undefined for quite a number of years, during which time no one would come to a decisive opinion, and no one would summon him for re-examination. He began to believe that the subject had been forgotten, that the incident might as well never have happened. He started to walk the streets confidently, even going into a barber's shop one day to have his long beard shaved off. He sat down on the comfortable swivel chair, gave his feet a relaxed shake, drew out an old newspaper from the pile on the table, and riffled its pages indifferently. But no sooner had he turned to the last page than his eyes widened in surprise. There was his own picture, printed at the bottom of the page among those of female suspects. Prostitution was not prohibited in those times; so they arrested him and returned him to service.

* * * * *

At that time, Hamida had found her way to an honourable profession (for in those days, 'honour' meant domestic service). She learnt the first lesson which such service demands: that one must call females by the term 'my mistress' and address males as 'my master'. She became aware that her master and mistress grew more satisfied with her the lower she hung her

43

head when passing before them, and her upper half began to take on a permanent stoop. The house protected her from the street, and in the street a man lay in wait, never ceasing to pursue her.

The kitchen was her life. More specifically, her life was the humid square patch in front of the basin, her small hands plunged in the water running from the tap, day and night, summer and winter. Her black eyes faced the wall, gazing from beneath a crust of dried tears that was dissolved from time to time by a blazing look, sharp as a sword, that pierced the wall and passed through into the dining room. That expression penetrated all the way to the round dining table surrounded by nine mouths, opening and shutting upon bulging jowls, jaws grinding, teeth clacking like the cogs of a mill-wheel.

In the basin, stacks of empty plates collect, covered by a film of congealed fat; the garbage pail is filled to the brim with untouched leftovers, while the sink drain becomes clogged with the half-chewed leavings.

At midnight, after mopping the kitchen floor, she crams a chunk of bread into her mouth, and gnaws on a bit of skin or a piece of bone that holds remnants of marrow. She settles herself, wet *gallabiyya* and all, on the wooden bench behind the kitchen door, her swollen, reddened fingers still oozing a yellow fluid with the warmth of blood. Her ears track the aggressive male hissing that emanates from the bedroom, followed by a submissive female moaning and the creaking of wooden bed joints.

As she sleeps, the fatigue drains from her body, the pain in her hands and feet abates, and her breathing settles into an intimate peacefulness through which glide familiar images that have lain dormant in some dark interior. A spent wisp of light still dances through those recesses, casting a faint glow that gives the walls the appearance of mud-brick, with its interspersed gleam of yellow straw. The walls climb to the

44

round, window-like aperture and drop to a floor covering which looks very much like that familiar straw matting. On one edge lies her mother, the black *tarha* wrapping her head, one hand pillowing her temple. On the nearer edge sleeps Hamida, lids half-dropped: the eyes of a child who has fallen asleep to the tones of a frightening bedtime tale. Her lips are half open over tiny, translucent teeth which have sprouted recently in place of baby teeth. Her breaths have the sweet, childlike smell given off faintly by closed blossoms just before the dew falls and dawn arrives. Beneath the full-cut *gallabiyya* her breasts show like two tiny buds that have emerged just moments before, to be compressed suddenly under the large hand, flat as an axe blade, which has begun to creep stealthily underneath the *gallabiyya*, raising it from the small legs and thighs. Everything becomes compounded into a single object, a single heavy stick in the shopkeeper's hand, striking blow after blow, over her head and chest and then between her thighs. And she screams, voicelessly; and she cries alone in the night in stifled sobs, and swallows her tears before dawn. Early in the morning, before anyone has awakened, she spits her tears into the lavatory, straightens up resolutely, and peers into the mirror at her tear-washed eyes, raised questioningly.

But no one answers her questions. No one responds to her slightly stooped back, her festering, swollen fingers, the cracked soles of her bare feet ascending the service stairs. The servants' stairs spiral crookedly; at every twisting bend is a dark crevice wide enough to hold a secret crime, and a garbage bin that has overflowed, filling the floor with flies and tiny cockroaches which crawl under the bottoms of doors into the elegant, well-appointed flats.

Yet an observer would see no marks of servitude upon Hamida as she climbs or descends those stairs. And what are the emblems of servitude? Tears have rinsed her eyes clean, and her gaze is directed upward: and nothing matters but the

45

eyes. Everything else may well be ulcerous and oozing pus;
Hamida may well be sunk up to the knees in garbage – animal
leavings, for her masters are among the carnivorous, and dead
flesh carries a smell more putrid than that of dead vegetation.
Hamida stamps the odour underfoot, and holds her head high,
and comprehends what no one else seems to understand.

What Hamida realizes is that one's garbage increases as
one's position in society rises. It is in the nature of things that
the stomach which consumes more from its upper orifice
expels more from below. And naturally, as her master's
stomach is undisputably the largest stomach around, his
refuse is the most abundant. The servants lug it to the bins,
and armoured vehicles cart it off to a distant spot in the desert,
where it collects in the shape of a high pyramid, to be gazed
upon by bedazzled tourists.

Small pyramids of garbage mark every street corner, visited
from time to time by rats, stray dogs, and small cats whose
round, gleaming eyes gaze upwards as if they are children, and
whose paws – festering like Hamida's fingers – search swiftly
and nimbly for a piece of bread and something to soak it in
which has not yet gone rotten.

Clasped around something, Hamida's fingers emerged from
the refuse bin. She opened her hand to see what it was, but a
sudden light fell over her palm, and she ducked behind the
wall. The light followed her, casting a long shadow across the
floor: a close-shaven head, shoulders broad and outlined by a
row of yellow buttons. Recognizing him at once, she gasped
loudly, and opened her eyes to the rough voice of her master.

'Hamida!' She saw the ewe coming through the door, driven
by the butcher, and realized that today was the feast-day
commemorating her mistress' death.

Her gaze met the ewe's eyes. The ewe planted all four legs
firmly on the floor and refused to move. Hamida stared into
the black spheres surrounded by pure white. Blanketing the

46

whiteness was an unexpected gleam that moved over the surface of the eyes, glittering, like a large, immobile tear which neither evaporates nor falls. Her eyes widened in surprise, with the consternation of one who has raised her head suddenly, only to see her own eyes in a mirror which had not been there before.

The butcher tugged the ewe by means of a short rope wound around her neck. The ewe followed him, but twisted her neck to the rear so that she still faced in Hamida's direction. The butcher's large, coarse fingers closed round the neck; the ewe's small hooves, front and back, lashed out at him. Four strong hands came out and pulled her forelegs and hindlegs apart. Now she lay stretched out on her back, her wide black eyes open in terror, searching in the eyes around her for her mother's eyes. Not far away, her mother stood motionless, eyes calm and steady, lashes unmoving, the black *tarha* quiescent over her head, shoulders and chest.

A long, slender muscle extending the length of the small, lean thigh trembled, and the tremor moved to the top of the thigh. It perched there, on the obtuse angle, looking like a child's open, panting mouth, its lips soft and rosy, dewy with a transparent saliva akin to children's tears, revealing beneath them the red hue of blood. The delicate tongue began to tremble, like the tongue began to tremble, like the tongue of a little bird being slaughtered.

She raised panicky black eyes once again to search for her mother's eyes amongst those crowding around her. Her mother looked at her with alien eyes, with a look cold as a knife-blade. She shifted her eyes to the ceiling, averting them from the blade, but the knife was coming ever nearer, little by little, until a lightning-quick movement split her in half.

Hamida did not feel the pain. Her eyes remained dry, and she abandoned herself to the dirt floor, lying there passively, while from beneath her thighs came a long ribbon of blood, its

47

dark red hue glistening in the sunshine. Ants appeared from nowhere to accumulate thickly over the blood-ribbon curved and inanimate like the back of a dead snake. She blew at the ants to scatter them, and sneezed as the dust penetrated her nose, ejecting the tears which had congealed in her throat. She reached out and covered the ants in dirt. Now that the blood had been buried, the previously level patch of floor was slightly mounded, like a grave. She pressed the sole of her foot over the protruding gravesite, trampled the uneven floor with both feet, paced over it with all her reclaimed strength. At the bend in the wall she twisted to look behind her. Finding no one there, she raised the *gallabiyya* from her legs. The familiar appendage was not there; in its place she found a small cleft, which looked just like that old, closed-up wound.

The familiar roughness of that voice reached her ears. 'Hami-i-ida.'

Hurriedly, she lowered her gown, hoisted the full water bucket and poured it over the ewe, cleansing her neck of the congealed blood. She hosed water into the ewe's slit gullet, and the spray gushed from her mouth and nose like a fountain. The seven children laughed in delight: for today was the feast, the ewe had been slaughtered, and the utensils, serving dishes and plates lay ready on the table.

The dinner hour arrived, and everyone sat down to eat; everyone, that is, except the mother, who had died in the bedroom, and Hamida, who was still hoisting the bucket, pouring water on to the dead body, filling her small palm with shampoo and rubbing it into the thick coat, inserting her small finger to wash the large ear. She raised the closed lids and washed the eyes, and then the nostrils. She cleaned the mouth and neck, the black hair under the ewe's legs, and her underbelly.

She washed the animal's thighs carefully, from below and above and in between. Her eyes wide in surprise: the space

48

between was smooth and sealed shut, showing no appendage. At the uppermost part lay a long cleft that looked like an old wound.

Her trembling fingers moved down to the hind legs; she pushed the loofa into the cloven hooves, to which remnants of soil still clung: black and clayey soil, streaked with yellow lines, like the straw with which animal pens in the village are strewn.

She heard the same harsh, commanding tones, coming from outside the door this time.

'Don't waste your time on the hooves, we'll give them to the butcher as alms.'

She grabbed the morning newspaper from the top of the bookcase and wrapped the hooves in it. On the front page she noticed a photograph. A crowd of round, fleshy faces filled the picture, and in the middle she recognized her master's features. They were sitting in a circle. The plates before them were full, piled high, pyramid-like; gleaming knives were plunging downwards methodically over the pyramids, which dwindled regularly and very rapidly until they had disappeared and only crumbs remained in the plates.

She thought the pyramids had faded away. However, when she scrutinized the newspaper with great care, she found them unchanged: piled high, tall, and tapering to sharp points. But now they were in another part of the picture, in another position between table and chairs, rising from below on two thighs to ascend as far as the obtuse triangle at the base of the ribs, directly under the heart.

Hamida's fingers slid over the smooth, slippery heart. The knife in her hand trembled as she cut the great artery and split open the heart so she could wash it from inside. How often she had done this with the hearts of chickens, rabbits, and geese – but the ewe's heart was much larger, and still very warm, its muscles yet pulsing, sending its hidden, trembling oscillation

49

through her fingers. The trembling moved into her arm, and then into her chest and all the way to her heart, which was beating more rapidly now.

From inside the split heart fell a deep-red clot of blood, which slipped over the marble edge of the basin and fell on to her foot. As she stooped to remove the clot, her eyes were caught by a long, thin, red ribbon that ran along her calf. She thought it was an artery, but in fact it was moving downwards over her skin rather than beneath. She touched it with her fingertip, and brought her finger to her eyes: it was wet with real blood.

As she straightened up, her alarmed eyes met her mother's: eyes empty of fright, cool as a brackish lake, silent as the grave, staring fixedly at her with the gaze of the dead. The lids dropped over the deceased eyes; the cover dropped over the head and body. She heard her mother's faint voice coming from afar, as if from beneath the ground.

'You've come of age, Hamida.'

Her mother handed her a pair of knickers made of brown calico. Hamida put them on under her *gallabiyya* once and for the last time, for as it happened she did not remove them with her own hands. Rather they were stripped off by other hands, by coarse and flattened fingers that bore a strange odour permeated by the scent of tobacco. Hamida knew the smell of tobacco: she used to buy it from the shop for her father or brother, or one of her uncles, or some other man from the family. It made her sneeze and cough whenever she brought it close to her nose.

When she coughed, the corners of her mouth would puff out like those of her father, and she would imitate his rough voice, and stand in the large entrance area of the house, just as he did, throwing her head back conceitedly as he did, inflating her jowls and placing her right hand firmly on her hip.

Were one to catch a glimpse of her at that moment, one

50

would think her Hamido. She herself used to believe she was Hamido. She would stride over the ground firmly, hitch up her *gallabiyya* over her thin hard legs, and run towards the boys, shouting, 'I'm Hamido.' They would play cops and robbers, or the train game, each of them grabbing the hem of the next, and taking off across the ground, whistling.

The whistle grows loud in the night. Hamida's small body shakes as she stands near the train. The darkness grows dense behind her, taking the shape of a large hand pushing her forcefully in the back, propelling her forward. Hamida darts off in the darkness, but almost immediately the darkness splits to reveal ten yellow eyes gleaming like brass buttons, and a sharp white blade hanging concealed alongside the long legs. She wraps her black *tarha* around her head and shoulders, chest and belly, and slips off in the evening blackness as if she herself is a piece of the night. But the legs run behind her, carrying their sharp blade, and the large feet advance with a sound that reverberates like the clash of iron against iron.

* * * * *

Hamido was still in the service. In the heel of his shoe was embedded an iron cleat which struck the asphalt slowly and heavily, like the hoof of a mule afflicted with sunstroke. The sun was afire: for it was an August noon in Cairo. Hamido's head, shaven utterly bald, seemed to attract the flaming red disc, for it clung to his pate. His eyes and nose had been reduced to boreholes that flung out the fire accumulated inside his skull. Ears, mouth, anus – all the orifices of his body shot out the red fire in hot, tiny lumps, congealed to hardness like old, clotted blood.

As he stared at the round, red disc, it turned into two red discs, inside each one a gleaming black sphere, like the pupil of an eye, surrounded by a circle of pure white as children's

51

eyes are. He stared at the pair of eyes: recognizing their particular shine, he shouted. 'Hamida!' He pulled the rigid implement upward from next to his thigh and aimed it exactly at the fixed point, halfway between the two eyes. He heard his father's rough voice.

'Fire.'

He fired.

The body fell, smeared with blood, the eyes open and fixed, gazing skyward. The gods had crowded the skies, seating themselves, one leg crossed over the other. Their upper legs dangled from amongst the clouds (and thus were visible to the naked eye) swinging with a regular horizontal movement, like that of a clock pendulum. The sun had disappeared and night fell; the music came on: the national anthem, in celebration of the victory. Palms were raised in applause, bearing the dead body upwards. The nose of the deceased brushed against the sole of a foot – belonging to one of the deities – and smelled the familiar odour emitted by feet whose owners do not wash them. The dead person averted his nose from the gods; the clamorous shouts ascended, and the black sheath split to reveal the badge of martyrdom in the battlefield of honour.

The dead person extended his hand, which was soiled with stains gone black (since the blood had dried) to receive the badge. Another hand – a clean, carefully manicured one – shot out and snatched the medal away. The dead person brandished his arm, sketching his anger in the air; the darkness was filled with searchlights, bulging from their sockets, their yellow glow spherical, looking like brass buttons.

Hamido's lips parted in bewilderment. His dead body fell among long legs, between which hung the hard killing tools; his bare foot was crushed beneath the high, heavy boots with their tall uppers. The ground became doughlike, and his other foot plunged in. Then his legs sank in – up to the knees, halfway up his thighs, as far as the top of his thighs, to the

52

middle of his belly. Little by little, he was sinking as far as the middle of his chest. The earth's grip closed around his neck, and his head went limp over the ground. He found the earth warm and tender, just like his mother's chest, so he buried his head between her breasts and managed to insert his nose under the left breast: his favourite, old, safe place. But his mother distanced him with her strong hand, as forceful as his father's. He lifted his head and saw his father's large hand, its long fingers grasping the badge; his wide, black eyes with their tiny red veins stared straight at Hamido. Hamido reached out; despite the dense crowd which constricted space and movement, his hand remained suspended in the air. Eyes stared at his bloodstained fingers, and no one shook his hand. (In those days, people scorned the slain and respected the slayer.)

Hamido was not a killer. It was he who had determined the point halfway between the two eyes and sighted, and he who had pulled the trigger, and he who had killed. But he slayed without becoming a slayer. For the slayer it is who carries the shame, yet whose own hands remain unsullied.

This shame was not Hamido's shame, though. All he had to do was to wash it away. (The distribution of special areas of expertise was one of the marks of progress, and so some managed shame and disgrace while others took care of the washing procedure.)

He pours the water from the bucket and washes everything carefully: hair, head, arms, legs, folds of skin around the hooves. He hears the imperious voice, coming from somewhere inside the house:

'Take the hooves – that's your share.'

So the hooves are lodged inside one of the daily newspapers, to enter history under the rubric of 'alms'.* Hamido carries them off under his arm, and walks along the street, visibly proud of them. From time to time, he peeks under his armpit, and there he sees the thick, black coat parting to reveal

53

a white, bloodless face, and the dead eyes dilated and turned skyward.

With an instinctive curiosity, Hamido stared into the sky. He noticed a lone, fiery star, as its long, thin tail moved shining over the blackness like a line of fresh blood which has not yet coagulated. Then a breeze came up and dried the blood, and the star turned black, and the sky became one motionless and impervious mass.

Hamido's head sank on to his chest; from his eyes trickled a hot thread, which descended to slip into the corner of his mouth, running beneath his tongue with the familiar, salty flavour of pickling juice.

He clamped his jaws together and swallowed the bitter fruit. There was nowhere he could take sanctuary from the loathing he felt. It was attacking him through all the passages and outlets of his body, injecting its bitter, salty taste through the cracks in his skin and the orifices of his body, accumulating in his recesses day after day, year after year, so that his insides took on the putrid sliminess of a jar that has long stored old, fermented cheese. Filling his mouth with black smoke, he would expel the air from his lungs and swallow nothing but smoke.

Hamida knew the smell of smoke, as she used to buy tobacco from the shop. But this time the smell was different, mingling with another, unfamiliar one. It reminded her, though, of the smell of the toilet after her master had shaved his beard. As her small fingers handed him the towel, she could see his eyes in the mirror: white and black alike dilated and radiating a brassy yellow light.

The light finds her and comes to a stop, even though she is hiding behind the kitchen door. Her small body shrinks inside her damp *gallabiyya*; her shoulders are uneven, the left one higher than the right. Her torso sags to the right from the weight of the vegetable basket, pulling her right arm down.

54

The toes of her left foot barely graze the blazing asphalt, while her right foot just brushes it with the back of her bare heel. An observer would think her lame. But Hamida is not lame: she is just hungry. So she reaches into the basket; her slim fingers slip under the greens until she feels the touch of the fresh meat. She tears off a strip of flesh and crams it between her teeth, quickly, before anyone can see her.

Hamida's teeth are tiny and white, but they are sharp, able to cut through raw meat and crunch the bones. These are primitive teeth, grown centuries ago, before the invention of knives and forks and other modern implements. (It was because of these implements that her master's teeth had lost their strength and his gums had been stricken with pyorrhoea.) Her eyes, too, are primitive and strong, able to spot objects from a great distance, and her ears can pick up any sound, no matter how far away. (Her master had also lost this ability, due to the secret police's discovery of modern hearing aids.)

Hearing a voice, Hamida raised her eyes, and saw her mistress' head peering out of her heavily decorated window high in the towering edifice. Because of the great elevation, her mistress' head was the size of a pinhead. Yet Hamida could see it clearly, and she took note of the fleshy muscle contracting beneath wide, hairy nostrils. She realized, from the way the hairs were trembling, that her mistress had picked up the smell of the meat she'd ground under her teeth. Hamida denied it, of course, but unfortunately for her, a tiny piece of meat had lodged between two teeth. Her mistress' tender-skinned fingers snatched it out with a pair of tweezers. In the full blaze of the sun, she donned her prescription spectacles, and examined the minute scrap as it lay on her open palm.

On this particular day, her mistress did not beat her. After a heavy lunch, a quarrel had broken out between master and mistress. It ended in agreement on the principle of women's equality to men in the supervision of servants. Thus, it fell to her master to carry out the beating this time.

Hamida lay down on the kitchen floor. Hearing heavy footsteps, she shut her eyes and waited. She felt the long fingers with their carefully trimmed nails lifting the damp *gallabiyya*, baring her small legs and thighs and buttocks, as far as the middle of her back and belly. Giving off a brassy shine, the yellowish eyes stared at the belly, throwing their citrine light over it: a belly stretched taut, its muscles contracting forcefully, falling to primitive thighs that could move in any direction, resisting and kicking out with full force. Her little foot propelled itself forward into the stretch marks of his flabby, protruding stomach. He grabbed her foot, and for the first time actually became aware of the shape of a woman's foot. This one had toes, five toes, each separated from the other. Her mistress' foot lacked toes; or, to be more accurate, her mistress' toes were stuck together, like a camel's hoof, in a single soft mass of flesh.

His hands crept over the legs. He felt the strong movement of the muscles pulsing under his palm. Her mistress' muscles never moved. Still and silent, they offered no resistance, as if his fingers were plunging into a sack of cotton (which wasn't surprising, as her mistress had already died, some time before, in the bedroom).

The movement of this living flesh dazzled him, as if he were a hog who suddenly comes out of a waste area in which it has existed on the remnants of carcasses for years. He shuddered deliriously, and his clothes fell from him. His warm body brushed the cold tile floor, still wet from being mopped. His lax, flabby muscles contracted, and an electric current flowed along his spinal column. Life stirred in all his senses; the broad nostrils of his trembling nose stole a whiff of garbage from beneath the basin. He inhaled as deeply as he could, filling his chest with the putrid odour. The smell ran through

56

his body and with it ran an old memory, from the days of childhood, of the first time he had experienced sexual pleasure.

But Hamida was cowering in the corner, clinging to the
wall, a tremor spreading over her body, and along with it an old
memory of her first beating. Her panic-stricken black gaze was
fixed on the stout bamboo stick. He had hidden it beneath his
clothes, or perhaps behind his back, and now he whipped it out
and raised it in her face, erect and hard. In a flash, he aimed it at
the fixed point halfway between her eyes. And pulled the
trigger.

Hamida screamed. Her voice reverberated through the
dark, silent night like the sound of a bullet being fired. Her
mistress tossed from side to side inside her silken shroud. A
few light sleepers bounded out of bed and turned on the lights.
Closed windows and doors were opened, and necks were
craned.

But the commotion led to nothing. The kitchen comprises
four walls, a ceiling and a door; on the door is mounted a steel
lock and chain. Everything returned to normal. Lights were
extinguished, windows and doors shut and locked. All things
were closed and locked. Stillness prevailed, and the darkness
collected over the kitchen tiles, growing denser in the corner
behind the door, in the shape of a naked little body beneath
which ran a long, thin, thread of blood, as a pair of tearful, wide
eyes shone childlike through the darkness.

* * * * *

Since early childhood, Hamido had been able to recognize this
particular glow from a distance, and, like starlight, it had
always drawn him. A solitary star lies wakeful and vigilant in a
uniformly black, impermeable sky, while Hamido marches
alone over the asphalt road, through the darkness, eyes
uplifted towards the star, arms folded across his chest so that

57

the old, black splotches of blood on his hands are visible. The sepia tones of tobacco stain his fingers, darkened under the nails to the colour of soil. His coughing fragments the night, and his white spittle bisects the darkness, landing on the asphalt in a ball, like a lump of white flesh streaked thinly with blood that comes to rest next to his feet.

They picked up his bloody trail, seized him, and returned him to service. The doctor lifted his calico drawers with fastidiously groomed fingertips, averting his face as the dead body's odour wafted through the room. He wrote out the diagnosis with his Parker pen: 'Suitable only for domestic service.' So Hamido became a house servant in the old style.

They took away the things in his custody: the iron-cleated leather boots, the suit and its cotton- and straw-padded shoulders, the yellow brass buttons – five across each shoulder and ten over the chest – and the wide leather belt from which hung his sheath, sheltering the blade that was sharp as a knife.

Hamido probed at his body in the darkness. He discovered that he was wearing the old, full-cut *gallabiyya* which now fell over his thighs loosely as would a woman's *gallabiyya*. His shoulders, now bony and no longer perfectly horizontal, were like the pans of an unevenly weighted balance. His right hand hung lower than his left, dragging with it the whole right side of his head and body. There's a simple and well-known explanation for this infirmity: house servants used to hoist vegetable baskets with their right hands. These baskets were always heavy, for they were filled to the brim with potatoes and tomatoes and artichokes. And in the bottom lay the slaughtered flesh, its warm, red blood seeping through the white waxed paper, its heart still quivering with an imperceptible movement, its ebony-coloured eyes open and looking upwards, tearful as they shone out in the darkness like the eyes of a child.

Bewildered, Hamido stared at the child's eyes. They didn't

have the characteristic glow of children's eyes; their shine was brassy, more like that of adults' eyes. The child clambered on to Hamido, thighs hugging his back and knees perched over his neck, one calf to each side, the heels of his shoes against Hamido's stomach.

The little one swung his legs as children do when riding donkeys. Hamido moved forward on hands and knees, the child on his back quivering in delight, a bamboo switch held tightly in his hand. The sun sat exactly halfway between the eyes, and the street was a mass of blazing red asphalt, overlain by fiery, crimson pebbles. When a flame-coloured pebble penetrated his right knee, Hamido paused to cough; the muscles of his chest were unable to contract and expel the pebble.

He hung his head, so that it nearly met his chest and he truly came to resemble an infirm donkey. The toe of the child's shoe, sharp as the tip of a knife, punched him in the belly, and he let out a cry. But his stomach muscles were unable to contract and expel the scream. He wrapped his arms around his stomach to protect it from the shoes, but then the child attacked him, biting him in the calf.

The fangs entered his flesh, and seemed to pierce his bones all the way to the marrow. He clenched his jaws and swallowed the pain. The agony accumulated in the bone marrow, hard and jagged like a piece of gravel. The child shrieked in delight and swung the toe of his shoe into the chip of gravel; it flew into the air and came to rest inside Hamido's belly, which was as warm as his blood-filled chest, or as his shaven head, which carried not a single hair to shade it from the sun.

The fire moved through his body. He submitted to it completely, letting it attack him from all openings. Assuming once again the bearing of a sickly donkey, he crawled forward, the burning taste of hatred invading him through the pores of his body to accumulate in its cavities, hardening and growing

59

crimson, until it would have looked like a live coal. He reached down to pull out the killing tool, and his fingers bumped against his inanimate thighs, their muscles hanging lax beneath the *gallabiyya*. He hid behind the kitchen door and raised his *gallabiyya*. Rather than finding the hard implement alongside his thigh, he was startled to see the cleft, black and scabbed-over, just like the old wound. His head fell over his chest.

The peremptory voice boomed out her name. Hamida extracted a hammer from behind the kitchen door. Her damp *gallabiyya* clung to her body, and a mark in the shape of a shoe was etched into the skin of her stomach. Under her stomach wall, hatred was growing like an embryo, rolling into a dough-like ball, rising day after day, swelling with water, fermenting and giving off its own particular scent.

The security apparatus picked up the smell, for there is always a security apparatus with watching eyes and sniffing noses somewhere nearby. Hamida held her breath and wiped the palms of her hands before stretching out one small hand to offer the glass of water from as far away as possible. Her master's neat, manicured hands closed around the crystal goblet. He averted his face from the smell, but it was so penetrating that it reached the dead nose of her mistress in the bedroom, causing the relaxed hairs in her nostrils to stiffen until they were sharp as pins.

Hamida denied it, of course. But her body was the crime. They took the body away and left her the crime. Like bees sucking at a flower blossom, they take draughts of the nectar and then reject the sucked-out remains. They tossed away the remains with a strong fling of the hand. The hand thrust into her back, feeling more like a kick. The road was dark, the night black, and she stared into the gloom. She recognized her mother's fist in her back, so she lifted her gaze to meet her mother's, and was on the point of calling out to her. But her mother was standing there motionless, even her eyelashes frozen in place.

Hamida walked by the stone statue and left it behind. Silence spread through the night and she realized that she was alone. She sat down on a stone bench by the Nile and filled her chest with the river's sad and sluggish air. The sadness entered her chest with the night-time gloom, and she knew that she had been born motherless, that her paternal grandmother had been a slave in her master's court and had died by her father's knife.

She let her body go limp on the bench, opening her pores to the attack of grief, which poured in to fill her completely and give her strength. Only rarely does sadness give; and then it earmarks a special kind of person for its giving, one who is able to exchange the offering. And Hamida was able to give herself completely to sadness. She could devote herself exclusively to it and live from it: eating and drinking it, digesting it so that its juice ran in her blood, to be sifted by her intestines and then secreted by her pores. It would trickle over her body like glistening threads, which she would lick off and swallow once again, to be digested once more, and secreted yet again.

To any passer-by, her erect stance, alone in the night, would suggest a Ramessid statue. A tongue of water moves over its cheeks, neck, shoulders, thighs, and feet, moving so gently that the motion cannot be sensed. The moisture remains on the skin, not evaporating despite the dry night breeze, but rather entering the pores, returning to whence it came, to its origins in the mother's womb. For it is sadness and cannot be mistaken for anything else. She and the everlasting embryo in her womb live for each other, and it comes and goes at her bidding. Whenever she wishes its emergence, it becomes her child – a natural child, not like the artificial children who from birth possess certificates inscribed in ink. In their bodies, black ink runs in place of red blood. Their sexual organs are

61

amputated, their hair is uprooted from their heads, and alongside every thigh hangs a toy pistol.

Her child has no familiarity with pistols, or dolls handmade of rags or straw, or any other toy: playthings are for children, and he is not a child. He is born standing on two feet; scrambling among the piles of manure, by himself, he laughs. It is this laugh which distinguishes him from children, for it is a soundless laugh that produces no movement in the facial muscles. His small eyes, though, are each coated by a tear which gives them a particular lustre. Beneath the tear a point of light diffuses, like a solitary star, wakeful and vigilant in a moonless sky.

Hamida walked through the night searching for her child. She circled the dung heaps. She looked behind the garbage bins. Next to the wall she spotted a little body huddled into a ball. She recognized him at once, and reached out into the darkness to enfold him to her chest. The darkness was cut by a yellow light and the brass eye appeared: always there is an eye watching, round and lidless, like a snake's eye, while the tail behind it is long and soft. The softness did not deceive her, though; she looked behind the tail. She saw the killing tool, hidden there, hanging alongside the thigh. It was not a male snake. Yet, even though she saw a female viper, Hamida knew that anything which kills must be male, and she screamed out to her child: 'Watch out for him, he'll kill you!'

The fangs entered the spindly leg. Like a long, thin tail, the blood flowed out, wetting her little toes, and running down to the soles of her feet. She raised her head, and saw her mother's wide, jet-black eyes fixed on her own eyes, looking at her mutely, the black *tarha* covering head and chest and belly. She opened her mouth to form her question, but the large palm was clapped over her mouth. Her breathing, the slight breeze, the rustling of the trees: all became a soundless, impermeable, black mass. The black *tarha* melted away into the night as a drop of water melts into the ocean.

But the legs pounded along behind her, towering above her like a high wave that followed her into the sea, constantly checking her position, plunging with her to the depths, and floating with her, a pair of corpses, on the surface. The wave lost itself with her in the middle of the ocean, then reappeared on shore, colliding with her against the edges of the rock, getting lost in the white foam, swaying with her between ebb and flow.

The flow was weak; the ebb was weaker. For the sea was not a sea after all, but rather the river Nile; its waters lay sluggish in the river bottom, their movement slow and heavy, like a half-paralysed foot that lies immobile once it is lowered to the ground. Hamido pulled the foot upward though, with all his strength, using all the muscles in his thin, bowed leg. Raised above the ground, the foot became fixed there, and would not descend again. But the ground pulled it back with all its force so that it fell heavily, like a foot carved from stone.

It was early morning; the sun was still slanting across the ground, and his shadow was sketched over the earth: long, thin, as bowed as a rainbow. The head was shaven and the shoulders uneven, one higher than the other. One leg was longer than the other, too: this was the frame of a lame man. Laughing, the children behind him were clambering on to his back.

The children's voices and screams hurl themselves at him from somewhere above his head, and their feet pound over his back like the wheels of a train. Each one grasps the hem of the next, and they whistle, and the whistling ascends in the air. Each of them runs to hide from the seeker – behind a dung heap, in the animal pen, or behind the lamp-post.

The lamp-post stretched so far into the sky that it seemed stuck fast to the moon. The moonlight fell on to Hamida, turning her face, arms, and legs white as she stood concealed behind the lamp-post. Her entire body shone pale, smooth and hairless. Only the roots of her plucked body hair protruded, becoming rigid with a shiver that spread across her skin.

She extended a white hand and touched her skin. Only her body could give her reassurance, for nothing outside it was reliable or secure: the world beyond consisted of strange bodies harboured in corners, behind walls and doors, in the darkened bends of streets, everywhere. Although the angles might seem smooth and innocuous from the outside, as if nothing lay within, when the sides of the triangle parted and the legs drew apart, the killing tool would emerge, clearly visible, hard and erect.

Hamida screamed, but the sound that emerged did not have the familiar timbre of a cry of fright or a plea for help. As a matter of fact, Hamida was not asking for anyone's help, since she knew that the road was empty of people. She was well aware that its windows and doors were shut and its lights extinguished. It was an area devoid of sounds, of voices, of everything.

No, it was not a scream for help; but it was sharp and long, going on and on as if it were in fact millions of screams coming together, welded into a single scream as endless as the night, and bonded in place with millions of the black particles from which the darkness and silence are made.

Nor was it a scream of alarm or fear. Hamida had no fear of the dark, or of silence, or even of death, for she was part of the darkness and her voice was the silence. And death has lived with her. She has borne it like a second body clinging to hers, like a second person, dead and living inside her. It occupies the emptiness within, enfolding its arms and legs, stretching itself out, its scent spreading outwards through her eyes and ears, from her nose and mouth, wafting from every opening in her body. At night, when the gloom intensifies and solitude

64

weighs heavier, she reaches out and feels him beside her, clinging to her; in her embrace his breaths mingle with hers, the heat of his body indistinguishable from her warmth.

Hamida planted her hand on her back, and a feeling of safety came over her. Were one to see her warm, soft, gently curved body from the rear, one would mistake her for a child. But as she turns around and her eyes grow visible, one sees unmistakeably that she is old. The faces of the elderly, like those of children, are sexless, but her growing belly, expanding with the live embryo, identifies her as a woman. One would be at a loss to determine her age, for Hamida is ageless. Such is the status of children born in defiance of the government employee who determines birth dates. They live untouched by the government, unaffected by history, unmarked by time and place. They do not pass through the stages of childhood, youth, and old age as do ordinary human beings. They live on, beyond old age, notwithstanding the government employee who records dates of death. Like the gods, they are spared the boundaries of time, and they live forever, sharing a single, extended existence unmarked by developmental stages.

Born as adults, they grow old without experiencing childhood or adolescence, and then move suddenly from old age to infancy, or from childhood to adolescence. They pass by in a single fleeting second, faster than the eye can see, for the human eye cannot fathom their essence. Such creatures appear as child, youth and old person at one and the same time and place. Sometimes they walk the roads when already dead, and when their smell is virtually unbearable. Yet the human eye remains incapable of distinguishing them from the living. Even wrinkles hold little significance in such cases, because they appear not as wrinkles but rather as the natural laughter lines which show on a child's face when it laughs forcefully but inaudibly.

Hamida was still standing behind the lamp-post, her face

65

swollen, round, and white as flour beneath the light, her wrinkles concealed by powder, and her cracked lips – chapped by hunger – glazed with a bloody, red crust. Her chest protruded from the opening of a torn gown, and her belly jutted out below. Her cracked heels were visible inside backless, slipper-like shoes. Her hair, as thick and black as a piece of the night, covered her head and chest, encasing her entire body in blackness. From within the blackness her white neck arched out, like a healthy tree trunk showing above the forest horizon, signalling that its roots are sunken deep into the moist ground.

An observer would think her a woman of the night, even though she was not a woman and the time was not night. The sun was directly overhead, at the exact midpoint between the eyes. Hamida was staring at the blazing red disc, unblinkingly, without the slightest twitch of a facial muscle, staring with all the patience she could summon. She saw him clearly at the centre of the circle, like a rainbow: long, thin and stooped, passing before her eyes with his characteristically slow gait, one shoulder higher than the other, one leg longer than the other – the frame of a lame man. She recognized him immediately and almost shouted out 'Hamido'. But she feared that her hiding place behind the lamp-post would thus be revealed, that he would recognize her swollen belly and pull out the killing tool.

She clamped her lips together and held her breath. But he smelled her anyway, for her odour was strong and penetrating, like that of the dead. He came to a stop, and stuck his long, thin hand behind the lamp-post, but it found nothing to grasp. 'Hamida.' The barely audible voice was familiar, an imitation of her own voice, in fact. He bent his trunk into a skilfully crafted imitation of her shape – for there had been great progress in craftsmanship, industry and technology. So skilful was his portrayal, that Hamida was confused into thinking the

66

voice was actually hers and mistaking the body as her own. She emerged from behind the lamp-post confidently, walking out with head bent, as usual. But as she lifted her head, her gaze clashed with the yellow eyes. So terrified was she by this surprise that she saw double. Then the four eyes multiplied with lightning speed, until yellow eyes surrounded her: ten marching down the chest and five along each shoulder, giving off a brassy yellow light.

The metallic voice bounced across the asphalt like the clanging of iron against iron. 'What's your name?'

'Hamida.' Her voice was barely audible.

The razor-blade moved over her head; her soft, thick hair fell into the pail. The razor dropped to her body, and passed over her skin, uprooting the hair. When it reached the pit of her lower stomach, moving through the patch of black hair it stumbled upon the tiny white bud that looked like a newborn bird. It plucked the bud from its roots, leaving in its place a deep wound in the flesh, like the scabbed-over cleft. (In those times, this surgical operation was called 'purification'; its goal was to 'purify' the human being by removing any remaining sexual organs.)

Hamida lay on the cement floor, surrounded by four cement walls, her arms and legs rigid and bound together into a single bundle. Between her thighs hung the iron padlock of a hard metal belt. (This has entered history as the chastity belt.) Its chain clanked dully against the cement floor whenever she moved a limb.

Beneath her, a pool of blood seeped through the cracks in the floor. The walls were splashed with blood in the shape of human fingers: old, black blood, like spots, millions of them, stains left by every age and race and sex: children, men, women, old folks, white, black, yellow, red. Everyone had a particular stain, an individual one shaped like the imprint of a hand.

67

Hamida stuck a small fingertip into the cleft; it came out wet with blood. She wiped it on the wall, imprinting her mark on the cement, like a personal signature. (Illiterate people – the likes of Hamida – all seal official documents this way.) Black, bloodstained fingers reached out to imprint their seal on the documents – millions of documents, bearing millions of seals, all black, their lines crooked and spidery like the legs of cockroaches, or flies, or locusts. Millions of insects, diffusing over the earth, night and day, on to bridges and city walls, at the bend of every street, behind every house and every wall, inside every crevice in the earth, their bare and shaven heads poking out across the surface of the ground while their skinny, bowed bodies remain inside the fissures. Their insides are hollowed out, empty of internal organs, devoid of livers, hearts, stomachs, intestines. The vast, empty cavity becomes a secret storage place packed tight with hatred. (In those days, only this spot was beyond the reach of the security apparatus. More recently, the military have made great advances; in the field of medicine, for example, they have invented x-ray equipment which reveals foreign bodies inside a human being, and an electronic speculum which is placed in the anus to reveal the contents of the internal cavity.)

X-rays fell upon her swollen belly, showing the cavity full to the brim with hatred, layer upon layer upon layer, millions of fine layers, like thin sheets of near-transparent metal massed on top of each other to form a solid bulk of hard metal. The doctor probed at her with his soft, carefully manicured fingers and let out a shout.

'Gunpowder!' The pickaxes rained down, breaking apart the earth, turning over the soil, inverting the very fissures they had made. They stumbled on the gunpowder stores, one and all. (History has celebrated the victory of x-rays over cancerous protrusions in the body.)

But cancer is a sly disease, more cunning than history, and

the tumour continued to grow deep inside the earth. When Hamida placed her hand beneath the womb, she felt the tumour, warm to her hand, giving off the heat of her body, and was reassured. She sniffed the familiar fragrance on her fingers – a scent reminiscent of the dung heap, the garbage bin, or the lump of dead flesh. She breathed it in fully: for it was the odour of her life.

Hamido turned his head in her direction, attracted by the odour they shared. Conceivably, he could have distanced himself and fled, but instead he approached her, by virtue of their shared lot. He halted beside the corpse, unrolling his tall frame and sketching the long, thin, crooked outline of his shadow on the asphalt. The white blade hung visibly alongside his thigh, its black, blood-like stains in evidence. He filled his chest with the night air, and realized that he had been born motherless, that his paternal grandfather had been a soldier in the army of Muhammad Ali* and that he had been slain in prison.

He knew suddenly – and as if it were an ancient verity as certain as death – that prison was his destiny. He offered no resistance, but let his body go limp in the iron grip. During the years of captivity, he had been drilled in the principle that relaxing the body lessens the strain it must undergo. Indeed, the tension had drained from his opened pores, from his eyes and ears and nose and anus. Now, nothing would seem quite as brutal, whether it was the beating, or the feeling of his body puffing up, or the branding by fire (at least, prior to the discovery of electricity).

His body falls limply to the ground, and he stretches out as fully as he is able. From beneath him stream thin trails of blood that slip into the crevices in the ground. The walls bear black stains that look like blood, every one in the shape of five fingers and a palm. Millions of stains, left by every age, every race, every sex: children, men, women, old people, white and black, yellow and red. And every one has his own particular, distinguishable stain.

Hamido rose from the floor, supporting himself against the wall, and imprinted his mark on the cement like a personal signature. (Those convicted – the likes of Hamido – seal police reports this way.) Black, bloodstained fingers reach out to imprint their seal on the police reports – millions of reports, stacked and heaped like corpses on Judgement Day (before the discovery of buses made such a crush of bodies an everyday occurrence). These bodies were aligned horizontally and arranged side by side in alternate directions – head next to rear and rear next to head – and so closely packed that they covered every inch of floor and ceiling. They were tightly compressed and so congealed together that no air could possibly penetrate, and no one could stretch out an arm or leg.

Hamido closed his eyes, opened his mouth, and moaned. The others followed his example, and millions of voices rose in the gloomy vastness, manufacturing the silence of night. The silence was so dense and heavy that it created a pressure on his ears, causing him to open his eyes. A pair of feet, the soles badly cracked, were almost touching his face. He recognized them at once and whispered, imitating her voice: 'Hamida.' But she did not answer: she was dead, her body sprawled on the ground, her face to the sky, the white moonlight falling upon it to give it the round and swollen aspect of an inflated bladder.

She opened her mouth and moaned (due to the pressure of urine). Millions of moans rose in the dawn and created the national dirge (which they used to call the national anthem).

Hearing the anthem, Hamido realized that morning had come. He dragged his legs out from under the iron girdle and walked to the latrine – the only place in the world where he felt optimistic. From behind the wall, he would exchange a few words with others, while his lower half would send out a

70

thread of urine, as thin and bowed as his frame, its odour as piercing as his. At this, he would feel suddenly and surprisingly mirthful; observing the yellow threads of water around him, glistening in the light like victory arches, he would let out a great roar of laughter.

The loud guffaws would ring out from the latrine, millions of them, for the numbers increased day after day. And in those days, all equipment was susceptible to breakdown, except that of reproduction and the wireless, of course. The sound would spread as any sound does, and at the same speed (by means of one of the instruments available at the time) to enter the large pair of ears like a sharp pebble. A clean, manicured finger would poke itself into those ears, and the sharp pebble would fall into his chubby, fleshy palm. Gazing steadily at the designated civil servant, he would inquire: 'Are they laughing?'

The civil servant would lower his eyes, as civil servants usually did in the presence of the big chief, Hamido's master: 'No, milord, they're just urinating.'

Hamido was still standing in the latrine. The thread of water had not yet expended itself when he saw the civil servant coming to carry out an inspection. He felt afraid; and fear, like death, is an organic being, composed of flesh and blood. He sensed the blood draining from his head, limbs, and internal organs, seeping downwards to collect at the pit of his stomach, in a single point that swelled to become as distended as his bladder. The civil servant still stood before him, legs planted apart insolently, eyes fixed steadily on him with the courage of civil servants in the absence of their master, mouth open to show ulcerous gums, afflicted with pyorrhoea (like his master's gums).

He felt a sharp pain low in his belly. He turned around. They were tightening their grip, and bodies were pressing in on him from every side, leaving no open space, yielding no room at all. The only empty space he could see was the

71

ulcerous open mouth, so he aimed the ribbon of water at it and emptied all the fear from his body.

Hamido opened his eyes. He could feel the pool beneath him, its warmth like that of his body and its piercing smell akin to that of his life. He realized that he was still alive and was quite hungry. He reached out, extending his hand into the shallow bowl. Millions of small black insects swarmed out, buzzing around him gleefully, some flying, others scuttling, still others crawling. A few clung to the ceiling and perched on the walls; others disappeared inside the cracks, and one alighted on his open palm.

He looked between its legs. Seeing there the old, scabbed-over wound, he knew it was a female, and that she was dead. He clapped his other palm over her, and she died again. He cracked her dead extremities and the recorder picked up the sound. (A tape recorder of the latest model, the size of a chickpea, had been fixed inside one of his body parts.) He cracked the toes of his own right foot with pride and self-esteem. His passage through history had significance, and this was why, when lenses were trained on the State's employees, he saw terror shading their eyes. For any movement they made would enter history instantaneously – even a mere cracking of a knuckle (due to the brittleness of one's joints after the age of forty) or a finger raised to brush away a fly that has perched on one's nose.

He gave his toes an innovative, creative shake. In spite of everything, he loved authenticity and originality, and despised imitation. What an accumulation of imitative, unauthentic, ape-like movements history has recorded! Identical faces, identical fingers and toes, one imitation after another, one imitation over and over again. An accumulation that grows ever vaster, higher and higher, just like a pile of manure. Every day, the cow lies down, and every dawn, his mother collects the dung, dumping it in a sunny place. By the next day, it is dry,

72

and on its way to becoming firmly rooted in history.

Finally, the treacle appeared, a congealed mass at the bottom of the bowl, which settled at the base of his stomach like a lump of tar. He chewed at a bit of onion, offsetting the sour taste of the bitter cucumber. He lit a wad of tobacco and filled his chest and stomach with smoke. Now he felt something akin to fullness, and belched in a loud voice that intimated self-confidence. (At that time, only males experienced this.)

Hamida heard the sound, and in it she recognized the smell of tobacco. After all, she used to buy tobacco from the shop for her father or brother or uncle or some other man from the family. The shopkeeper would hand her a sweet, which she would pop into her mouth, hiding it under her tongue. When he demanded the penny from her, she would open her hand and find nothing; she would open her eyes and find the lamp, like a wisp of light, flaring up only to die out at a single gust of wind. And darkness would fill the door, like a tall, huge body, solidly dark except for two round holes at the top of the head from which pierced a red light, the colour of the pre-dawn.

'Who are you?' she whispered, in a frightened, nearly inaudible voice. He answered in the same tones. 'Hamido.' She closed her eyes so that he would not recognize them; she let his long arms enfold her, and his hot breaths warm her. It was winter, and her ears, so soft and small, were like shells of ice.

He whispered, expelling a hot breath into her ear. 'Who are you?' She remained motionless, her ear still below his mouth, and gave no response. She pretended to be asleep; she hid her head in the thick hair on his chest. When she felt the large fingers raising the garment from her body, she held her breath. Her chest no longer rose or fell. She had turned into a corpse.

But in the morning, the slanting sun fell on her eyes. She saw the lank form beside her, noted its thin and crooked shape. His shoulders were uneven, resembling hers; his fingers were swollen and festered from washing dishes, like hers, and the fingernails were just as black. She knew at once that it was her own body, so she hugged him with all her strength, and pressed her chest to his, and felt the outlines of the leather wallet just beneath her left breast. She was hungry, so she slipped the wallet from his pocket quickly, before anyone could see her.

She hid behind a wall and opened the wallet. She saw her portrait: encased in the black *tarha*, she resembled her mother on the night of her wedding. She found a directive in her father's handwriting, reminding him to wash away the disgrace, and four pounds and a *bariza* (in those days, a *bariza* referred to a ten-piastre coin or note).

The *bariza* bought her a meal, and with two pounds she purchased a mini-dress (the sort of shrunken dress popular in those days among chaste and virtuous wives, since the only parts of their sacrosanct bodies exposed by such garments were the arms, shoulders, bosom and thighs). With the remaining two pounds she bought a pair of open-toed shoes with spike heels. (The emergence of open-toed shoes in that era was aimed at revealing the blood-red nail varnish worn by women; but these shoes had backs so that the cracks in women's feet resulting from domestic service would be hidden.)

Hamida walked down the street, teetering on her high heels, her arms, thighs and throat bare, her dress cut low to reveal her breasts. She had come to resemble her mistress, and although she walked right by the *shawish* (the widespread term for policemen in those days) he did not arrest her. In fact, as she passed before him undeterred, he lowered his head, and kept his eyes on the ground. (This was called 'averting the glance' and was practised before matrons of unblemished reputation. He had learnt the manoeuvre during his years of training.)

Holding her head aloft, she moved on with swaying,

74

tottering steps. She swung her bare shoulders, the left one appearing to be higher than the right. Her left breast was higher than her right breast (due to the swollen wallet concealed beneath her left breast) and her buttocks, one higher than the other, shook as she continued on her way.

She drew a few steps away from the policeman and ran her hand over the wallet. Its leather had the soft feel of saliva trickling over one's fingers after eating a sugared pancake. A stream of warm blood was moving from her left breast to her belly and on to her thighs and feet, and then ascending to her head, ears and nose, and falling once again to her heart, following its normal, repeating circuit and sending into the motionless cells a new impulse that gave her a pleasurable sensation.

She worked her jaws, and chewed the pleasure until it melted into her saliva and she swallowed both. The pleasure mingled with her blood and circled from head to foot, from feet to head. Her head began to spin, and she leant back against a lamp-post. Her lids drooped, so that the street grew dark and the sky turned black and moonless. The circular blue light fell over her face, and she recognized it at once. (Her master always painted the headlamps of his car blue to avoid being seen or recognized by anyone during his nightly rovings.) He opened his door and got out, walked round and opened the door for her, waited until she was seated, shut the door and circled round the car again, reached his own door, opened it, sat down, and shut the door. (Her master had been trained in this circular motion in the Faculty of Arts and Protocol.)*

Her spike heels were plunged into thick carpeting, soft as dough, and her shoes came off, revealing her cracked heels. She hid them under the silken coverlet. Her body had settled into a horizontal position on something soft – softer than dough – and she relaxed the muscles in her buttocks, which her long period of standing behind the lamp-post had strained. Her body began to sink into the dough: feet, legs, thighs, chest, all the way to the neck. Only her head remained visible, sticking up over the surface.

Her head began to sink gradually: chin, mouth, nose. Her eyes dilated with terror as she realized she could get no air. And terror is an organic being, composed of flesh and blood. It was personified before her now in the shape of a strange, misshapen creature with the head of a human being and the body of an ape. Its head was bare, shaven to sleekness, its chest a forest of hair, its buttocks as bare and smooth as its head, the skin on its backside showing the same transparent blood-redness as the face. The creature had reddish lips, parted to show a long, sharp tongue, just like a white blade with a hard metallic edge, at its tip a darkened hole in which death was lying in wait.

She screamed – her suppressed, inaudible scream – and dropped her eyelids over the terror. But it crept into her throat (through the lachrymal canal which connects eye and ear) and sat there, rolling up into a lump. She tightened the muscles of her throat and spat as forcefully as she could, so that thin threads poured fountainlike from her mouth, nose, and ears.

Her master laughed with a childlike delight that propelled his fleshy cheeks upwards so that his eyes were squeezed completely shut. She realized that he would fall asleep in a moment. (The royal salute had rung out, announcing the end of the jamboree.) As his snoring filled the air, she undid the golden buttons on his chest and lifted out the heavy leather wallet that had been pressing against his chest.

Opening the door quietly, she got out and made her way – slowly and assuredly – to her own car, which she unlocked with a gleaming silver key like the one her mistress had had. The car slipped over the soft asphalt like a graceful skiff gliding through the water. She passed alongside the policeman, his stance as erect as the lamp-post. He quivered (as if an electric shock had shot through him) and raised his right index finger to touch his left ear (a sacred movement in those days which symbolized love of country).

She stuck her head outside the car window. The moonlight fell on her face. The road was empty except for the lamp-posts, standing erect along both sides of the road. To the right, arms were raised high, and to the left, a finger was held to every ear.

She recognized the black stains on the finger, and whispered: 'Hamido!' But Hamido heard nothing, and remained stiffly upright, his head raised to the sky and one black finger to his ear. (Those travelling abroad used to see this memorial to the unknown soldier erected at the entrance to every capital city.)

Hamida stretched out her hand and grabbed his. His fingers were like hers, and the lines on his palm resembled hers. In a rush of sympathy – for their lot was a shared one – she tried to bend his arm downwards. But the stone arm, raised wearily, would not move. She raised her eyes and noticed that the wide ebony eyes shone with a real tear, a childlike one. The tear fell on to her cheek, still hot, and crept into the corner of her mouth and under her tongue, bitter to the taste. She swallowed it. Another hot tear fell on to her cheek and ran into her nose, just as bitter, so she swallowed it. Grief began to attack her from all sides, through every pore and orifice, pouring into her nose, mouth and ears like a soft powder. But the particles were sharp, like pieces of splintered glass, and they ripped apart the thin membranes that lay at the back of her nose, mouth and bronchial passages. She coughed violently, and from her chest oozed a white fluid that ran through a long narrow channel connecting heart to throat to nose to ears to eyes. She was ejecting mucous from her eyes, and spitting tears from her nose and mouth and ears, white substances jetted through with hairlike streaks of blood.

She raised her face to the moonlight, which had become

intensely white and devoid of blood streaks. Her features were strange; in fact, it was their contradictory nature that attracted attention. The chin was small, rounded, and soft like that of a child, while the forehead protruded, rough and wrinkled like an old person's brow. The lips were virginal, parted in a deprivation not to be satisfied – like the lips of chaste wives. The cheeks bulged with a sharp and insatiable gluttony – like the cheeks of respectable husbands. The nose was straight and upturned in self-pride, with the insolence of criminals and those outside the law, while the ears were small, submissive, and motionless, like those of government employees. The eyes were black and wide, bearing a primitive and shameless look, uplifted and steady, not averting their glance as the eyes of modest women do, as they gaze downwards, bashful and ashamed of their impertinent thoughts.

Strange features they were, and utterly contradictory. Even stranger, the contradictory nature of the features harmonized with the features themselves, in a balanced and familiar manner. In fact, the harmony and balance were so remarkable as to attain a degree of appeal whose very unfamiliarity captured attention. It was as if these features marked not one face but two or three or four, or as if the face was not even a face but something else.

This was a something else that stirs up confusion and bewilderment, and anxiety, and indeed, even anger. Naturally, a person grows angry if, looking into the face of another, he sees not the other person's soul but rather his private parts. And, naturally too, one's anger intensifies if the form of these private parts is unfamiliar or unnatural. For it is in the nature of things that private parts have a shape which inspires shame and offends honour – as well as carrying the odour of filth (not unlike the smell of sweat, urine, or any of the body's other poisonous discharges). But for them to have a sweet scent is strange indeed, for this indicates that the body is retaining its sweat and poisons. Very soon its insides will become putrid and give off the odour of filth. The face, though, will remain clean and white, adorned by features that demonstrate nobility as well as ancient and respectable family origins (and other such refined characteristics, as delineated clearly in the faces of noble people – the likes of her master).

Her master's face turned in her direction as she stood in the moonlight. Her dark and wide-open eyes returned his long gaze, not averting or dropping their gaze. He was so angry that he wanted to spit in her face. But he had grown so accustomed to concealing and suppressing his anger that it could no longer motivate any facial movement, except for a sudden contraction of one small muscle at the angle of his nose, which pulled his lips apart in what would seem – to the naked eye – to be a smile.

Since she had no other appointment, she climbed into the car. They passed along the façade of his chief residence in Zamalek.* She saw her mistress gazing down from the high, heavily-ornamented window. Although her head was the size of a pinhead (because of the great elevation) he could see her. Hiding his face with his right hand, he stepped on the accelerator and the car shot off before anyone could spot him. He drove slowly along Nile Street and crossed the bridge; now he was entering the quarter of Bulaq,* where he had his secondary residence. (Every respectable husband at that time had a secondary residence in addition to the main one, and the number of his secondary residences increased in proportion to his rise in position.)

He stripped off his clothes promptly (as is the habit of those involved in important matters) then raised his foot and placed it on the edge of the bed, his other foot remaining on the floor. (He had been trained to stand on one leg during his years of public service.) By coincidence, at this very moment she turned towards him; she found not the killing tool but rather the old, closed-up wound. One might have expected her to register surprise, but apparently she had seen nothing to disconcert her, for she swung her head back towards the wall indifferently. There, inside a gilt frame, she saw her mistress in military garb. Her mistress' eyes were settled upon the naked heap, and she followed its movements with the sedate, even grim, look of a magistrate, all the while snapping photos from every angle. (N.B. these pictures have been preserved in the archives of the Bureau of Intelligence.)

Thus, Hamida's face became well-known indeed. Whenever she peered from the car window, necks were craned in her direction – though heads were lowered, of course. Her face was plastered on walls, and erected at every street corner. That was where she used to stand and wait, and sometimes, when the waiting seemed to stretch out endlessly, she would look up and see her picture hanging there, lips parted in an expansive smile, while from the corner of her mouth, a long, white thread of warm saliva ran upwards to the edge of her nose and then edged towards the space between nose and eye.

With the palm of her hand, she would wipe the moisture off her face and then wipe her hand on the wall. There, sketched on the wall, would appear the palm and five human fingers. As the night breezes blew over it and the sun rose on it, the hand would dry out, turning into black stains the colour of old blood.

The sun's rays fell over Hamido's eyes as he slept upright beside the wall. He opened his eyes and saw the palm and black, extended fingers. Her fingers were like his, and the lines on her palm resembled those on his. His lips parted, calling out: 'Hamida!' He pulled the killing tool up, from alongside his thigh, but just then he caught a glimpse of the shining silver key dangling between her fingers, and realized that she was his lady mistress. He hid the implement in his pocket in the blink of an eye, let it hang loosely behind his thigh, and stood in his place erect, the muscles of his back taut and his right arm raised, his eyelids relaxed and dropping over his eyes like a curtain.

When the sound of the car had grown distant, he opened his eyes to see its tapered back bisecting the darkness which then swallowed it. He relaxed his back muscles, let his arm fall, and felt at ease. He filled his chest with the night air, and tried to remember what he looked like as a child – the shape of his features when he smiled or laughed – but he could recall nothing. There was no childhood to remember, no smile, no laughter.

He heard his own heavy footfall on the ground: right, left, right, left. Lub dub lub dub. Slow, regular beats, interposed by periods of silence as black as death. He coughed and spat out a lump of blood-tinged saliva. The bamboo switch fell on to his back; its sting told him he was naked and had not yet died. He lost his sense of optimism and spat again. Hearing the commanding tones of that familiar voice, he pulled the implement from its black sheath, and sighted carefully on the point midway between the two eyes. The harsh voice shouted, 'Fire!' He fired.

The tall, crooked body dropped; a long thread of blood streamed from a hole exactly at the midpoint of the knobby protrusion on the centre brow. The blood cut across the figure's eyes, cheeks, nose, and lips, to circle his small, rounded, childlike chin.

He was not one child, but rather thousands or millions of children, whose bodies had tumbled on to the asphalt. Every child's face was marked by a long thread of blood that ran from eyes to nose to mouth and the reverse. The sun fell over the asphalt, the sky turned a pure blue, and the gods came into sight, massed together, sitting in rows, one leg over the other, smoking from a waterpipe.

Hamido stretched out his leg; it collided with another leg.

He extended his arm; it bumped against another. He was drowning in a sea of dead bodies. He began to swim, using both arms and legs, through the vast ocean. He stopped for a moment to catch his breath, and turned around to find out where he was or who had brought him here. He remembered nothing except that he had been a child, and that a strong fist had pushed him in the back and hurled him into the sea. He saw the hand sketched on the wall: a large palm like his father's, but with fingers that were swollen and cracked like his mother's. His lips parted; he shouted. 'Mama!' His mother's black eyes looked at him, the black *tarha* covering her head and neck, shoulders and belly.

She was standing not far away, her tall frame motionless, the rise of her chest firm and still next to his head. He put his head on her chest, and buried his nose between her breasts. But his mother's strong hand pushed him away, causing him to glance up in her direction. There he saw his father's wide eyes, the red streaks gleaming like thin snakes over the whites, and he heard his father's coarse voice.

'Only blood washes away shame.'

He approached his father, staring steadily into his eyes. The red streaks over the large whites trembled. (A person takes fright if he sees an open eye gazing at him unblinkingly, for such a stare means that the eye is examining him thoroughly to see him as he really is.)

His father backed away, and with just one step to the rear, the lamplight fell squarely on to his face. He brought one big palm upwards to hide his face, but the light exposed his tall, large body as he stood there, blocking the door. He blew at the wisp of light, and it went out. The darkness now became so dense that it was impossible to distinguish the floor from the walls, or the walls from the ceiling. His large, bare foot stumbled on the slight rise of the threshold. But he regained his balance, and sprang forward pantherlike on tensile feet. He

82

moved on, slowly and cautiously, stepping over something which looked very much like the backless leather slippers worn by men in the countryside.

Hamido shrieked, his voice childlike; but his body was not that of a child. His hand plunged into his pocket, which was as long as a sheath, and drew out the hard metal implement. He determined the spot halfway between the white circles, over which the red threads glistened, and sighted. He held his breath, and shut his eyes, and pulled the trigger.

He opened his eyes and saw the tall, bowed body stretched out in the sun, its dilated eyes turned upward and its right arm dangling to the side, grasping something. Hamido opened the fingers, and the penny fell into his palm. He closed his hand over it, and went to the shop to buy tobacco. He bought a sweet and put it in his mouth. He turned to go back, but the shopkeeper asked him for the penny. He opened his closed hand and found nothing. The shopkeeper snatched up his stick and set off behind Hamido at a run.

As small and light as it was, his body could fly through the air like a sparrow. No doubt he would have been able to stay ahead of the shopkeeper (aah, had he only been a real sparrow!) ... But a feeling of heaviness came upon him, suddenly and just the way it happens in dreams. He felt his body grow sluggish; it seemed to have turned into stone, into a statue whose feet are planted on the ground and whose arms are fixed in place with iron and cement. His thighs, pulled apart, seemed to have turned into marble. In each foot was rammed a nail, as if he had been crucified. The bamboo switch swung into the air, long and thin and curved like a bow, and rained down on something soft and warm, like living flesh.

* * * * *

When Hamido opened his eyes, daylight was filling the room.

He thought for sure that what he had seen had been nothing but a dream. He jumped up from the mat and ran out into the street. His friends – all children of neighbouring families – were playing as usual in the narrow lane extending along the mud-brick façades. Each child grasped the next one's hand, forming a ring that circled round and round. The thin, high-pitched sound of their singing orbited with the movement of their bodies, yielding a single song, comprised of one stanza which repeated itself in a never-ending, unbroken cycle:

Hamida had a baby,
She named him Abd el-Samad,
She left him by the canal bed,
The kite swooped down and snatched off his head!
Shoo! Shoo! Away with you!
O kite! O monkey snout!

Because they were circling and singing uninterruptedly, it was impossible to pick out the song's beginning or end by ear, just as it was impossible to tell by looking where the circle began and where it ended. For they were children, and when children play they grasp each other by the hand to form a closed circle.

* * * * *

But everything does have an end, and so I must end this. Yet I do not know the end point of my tale. I am unable to define it precisely, for the ending is not a point that stands out clearly. In fact, there is no ending, or perhaps it would be more accurate to say that the end and the beginning are adjoined in a single, looping strand; where that thread ends and where it begins can be discerned only with great difficulty.

Here lies the difficulty of all endings, especially the ending of a true story, of a story as truthful as truth itself, and as exact

84

in its finest details as exactitude itself. Such exactitude requires of the author that he or she neither omit nor neglect a single point. For even one point – a single dot – can completely change the essence of a word in the Arabic language. Male becomes female because of a single dash or dot. Similarly, in Arabic the difference between 'husband' and 'mule', or between 'promise' and 'scoundrel', is no more than a single dot placed over a single form, an addition which transforms one letter into another.

Hence the importance of a well-defined point, that is, a real point in the full geometrical sense of the word. In other words, scientific accuracy is unavoidable in this work of art which is my novel. But scientific accuracy can corrupt or distort a work of art. Yet that corruption or distortion is exactly what I wanted, and what I aimed for in this story. Only then would it become as truthful, sincere and real as 'living life'. For some of the time, life may be dead, like that life which inhabits a person who walks through life without sweating or urinating, and from whose body no foul substance emanates. One who is truly alive cannot imprison his foulness within, or else he will die. Once he is dead, his face will become purest white, while his insides remain putrid, stained by the rottenness of death.

I fancied (and my fancy, at that particular moment, amounted to fact) that one of the children who were circling round as they sang in unison suddenly moved outside of the circle. I saw the small body come loose from the steadily revolving ring, breaking the regularity of its outline. It moved off like a gleaming speck, or a star that has lost its eternal equilibrium, detached itself from the universe, and shot off at random, creating a trail of flame, like a shooting star just before it is consumed in its own fire.

With an instinctive curiosity, I followed his movement with my gaze. He came to a stop so near to where I stood that I could see his face. It wasn't the face of a boy, as I had thought. No, it was the face of a little girl. But I wasn't absolutely certain, for children's faces – like those of old people – are sexless. It is in that phase between childhood and old age that gender must declare itself more openly.

The face – oddly enough – was not strange to me. So familiar was it, in fact, that it left me feeling bemused, and then my surprise turned to disbelief. My mind could not accept the sight before my eyes. It is just not plausible that, leaving home in the morning to go to work, on the way I should run head-on into another person only to discover that the face which met my gaze was none other than my own.

I confess that my body shook, and I was seized by a violent panic which paralysed my ability to think. Even so, I wondered: why should a person panic when he sees himself face to face? Was it the extreme eeriness of the situation in which I found myself, or was it the almost overwhelming familiarity of the encounter? At such a moment, one finds everything becoming utterly confused. Contradictory or incompatible things come to resemble each other so closely that they become almost identical. Black becomes white, and white turns to black. And the meaning of all this? One faces, with open eyes, the fact that one is blind.

Notes

Abd el-Samad: male name, literally 'Servant of the Ever-lasting', but *sumuud*, from the same root, also suggests 'defiance' and 'resistance'. According to the author, this song is sung by peasant children, and accompanied by a ring dance; as they reach the line 'Shoo! shoo!' they may throw stones outward from the circle.

Gallabiyya: an ankle-length gown or robe which is cut to hang loosely; it is worn traditionally by both men and women, although the style, colours, and cloth differ.

Muhammad Ali: (1769–1849) Born in Kavalla, Macedonia, he came to Egypt in 1801 as a soldier in an Albanian contingent attached to the Ottoman Turkish army. Triumphant in the power struggles which followed the French, then British, evacuation of Egypt, he was named Pasha/Ottoman Viceroy of Egypt in 1805 and ruled until 1848. Founder of the dynasty that ruled Egypt until just after the 1952 revolution, Muhammad Ali instituted reforms aimed at expanding Egypt's military power; these reforms, centring on education as well as industrial and agricultural development, had the effect of strengthening the country's economic base.

Zamalek: An island in the Nile at Cairo which has been a well-to-do residential and business area since the turn of the twentieth century, and where many of the foreign embassies have been sited. Traditionally, Zamalek has had a relatively large proportion of foreign residents, and has often served as a symbol of wealthy urban Egypt with its foreign alliances.

Bulaq: An old port on the east bank of the Nile, opposite Zamalek and just north-west of the old city of Cairo, which in the nineteenth century became an industrial area. Since, it has developed into a densely-populated and largely working-class residential and business area of the city.

Alms: specifically, *zakat*, in Islam the religiously prescribed obligation of giving alms to the poor; it is considered one of the five 'pillars' or basic practices that all Muslims are required to carry out to the best of their abilities.

Faculty of Letters and Protocol: The author puns on the several meanings of *adaab*, as 'etiquette', as 'morals', and as 'arts' or 'humanities' in the context of higher education. The singular, *adab*, means both 'literature' and 'good manners'. *Kulliyat al-adaab* is 'The Faculty of Arts' in a university.